Under
The
Skin

UNDER THE SKIN

A DERMATOLOGIST'S FIGHT TO SAVE THE NHS

ALEX ANSTEY

First published in 2022 by Alex Anstey

Copyright © Alex Anstey 2022
Illustrations © James Nunn 2022

ISBN 9781915036162

Also available as an ebook
ISBN 9781915036179

And audiobook
ISBN 9781915036155

Typeset by seagulls.net
Cover design by Emma Ewbank
Project management by whitefox
Printed and bound by CPI

CONTENTS

THE AUTHOR:
PROFESSOR ALEX ANSTEY

Now a dermatologist at the Royal United Hospitals in Bath, I started working for the NHS in 1983, and have been a consultant dermatologist since 1994. In 2000 I led the NHS team that won the UK Dermatology Team of the Year award. I was appointed as honorary professor of dermatology at Cardiff University in 2005, advisory professor of dermatology to Jiao Tong University, Shanghai, China in 2009 and honorary professor at Bangor University in 2021. As editor of the *British Journal of Dermatology* from 2013–2019, I led an overhaul of the journal, which rose in the international rankings under my stewardship. Medical education has always been more than an interest for me; I am a Fellow of the Academy of Medical Educators. *Under the Skin: A Dermatologist's Fight to Save the NHS* is my first book.

I have travelled widely, including backpacking from New York to Rio de Janeiro in 1978, then Nairobi to Cape Town via Kampala in 1981. I spent a three-month sabbatical from the NHS at Groote Schuur Hospital in Cape Town in 2005. I enjoy live music and saw Carole King in 1972, Bob Marley and the Wailers in 1975, The Who in 1976, David Bowie in 1977 and

1983, Miles Davies in 1981, Talking Heads in 1983 and Prince in 1985 and 2008 (and many more). I attend Glyndebourne Opera most years, and am a friend of the Welsh National Opera and the Bayreuth Festival in Bavaria. My football team Crystal Palace are consistent: each new season starts with hope and ends with disappointment.

My wife Sarah and I live in Bath. When not working I enjoy gardening, reading, walking and listening to music. We have two children, Rebecca and Ben, and a small dog called Moli.

AUTHOR'S NOTE

I have written this book from personal experience; the events described actually happened. They are, of course, my version of these events, and others may disagree with what I remember and how I have interpreted it. I have done my best to be candid and to treat the truth with respect. My intention was to create something worthwhile and authentic, which would resonate with readers, and stand the test of time. As an academic, I am well aware of the potential for coming to the wrong conclusion when relying on just one piece of evidence. I have therefore made every effort to triangulate; that is, try to obtain at least three perspectives on key issues in order to get closer to the truth. I have also based my own opinions and hypotheses on expert opinion. My ten experts and influencers had valuable insights which I have ruminated upon, before adopting and adapting them for my own situation.

I had various sources of information to complement my memories of the events described in this book: my old diaries, stretching back over thirty years, and my reflective diaries started during GP training in the late 1980s. I used other sources too, including the memories and opinions of others; expert opinion in the form of books and papers; expert opinion from top medical journals; and dependable, independent media. When I started writing this book, I was not expecting my memory to be reliable or clear about events long past. How wrong I was. I immersed myself in each story, cross-referencing with newspapers, books, listening to relevant music from that era, thinking about the sounds and smells and emotions of the time, rock and jazz concerts I had attended, remembering football games, the Olympics, the football World Cups; it all came back to me. The memories were there, just hidden from view; gentle coaxing and encouragement was all that were needed to get them to come out and play. It was a thrill to relive these events and to reflect again on what it all meant. It has been like living my life for a second time.

The patient stories are all made up. Any resemblance to people living or dead is purely coincidental. These case reports may seem real; that's because the situations they describe are real. But the patients themselves do not exist. They are a product of my imagination. It had to be like this; I have sworn an oath of confidentiality, which I respect. There are some clinical cases and situations where the events described are real, but have been altered to protect patient confidentiality. This has been done with the permission of the patients concerned. There are also some events where names and places have been changed to protect the identity of the protagonists. Again, the events described are real, but the places and names are made up. This is in order to be compliant with my duty as a doctor towards my colleagues and patients; to be honest, truthful and to treat them with respect.

I have used critical readers to help develop the text: other dermatologists; patients; lay people; a BBC journalist; my brother and brother-in-law; my editor; sixth-formers hoping to study medicine at university. I have also sought verification from key protagonists in the story, not by letting them rewrite what I had written, but asking them to read certain chapters or sections where they were involved, to check that the text was true and accurate, as far as it could be. Having established beforehand that they were willing to receive a draft of my book, I also sent copies of the whole manuscript to some 'higher-ups', including Andrew Goodall, CEO of NHS Wales; Jo Whitehead and Professor Arpan Guha, the CEO and medical director of Betsi Cadwaladr University Health Board; and Dr Bethan Jones, associate medical director for primary care in the West area of our health board, the area that hosted Dermatology Integrated Care. The feedback from these individuals was positive and constructive. I enjoyed these interactions, and would like to thank all concerned for the hours they have spent reading, thinking about and commenting on what I have written.

In 2006 Julian Tudor Hart published *The Political Economy of Health Care: A Clinical Perspective*. He was nearing the end of his life, and was expressing dismay at the creeping privatisation of the NHS: 'They have had to do it by stealth,' he said, 'proclaiming each successive capitulation to commerce as support for otherwise declining NHS standards. No open electoral battle has ever been fought, but the slide back to the market continues, driven by its own idiot logic of the bottom line, where profit stands proxy for every other outcome.' My own book describes the NHS austerity years which followed four years after Tudor Hart's book was published, where health service funding was aggressively restrained like never before, at the very moment when a market economy was introduced for the NHS in England. Tudor Hart would have hated it. And then, in 2020, came the ultimate test: how would the NHS perform in the face of a global pandemic following years of decline? Badly, is the short answer. The NHS has now lost its lofty position as a health service once globally admired; not many NHS clinical staff currently believe that our way of doing healthcare is world-beating, the best, to be copied and emulated. Indeed, it is now us who are casting around, searching for answers to learn where we have gone wrong and to start playing catch-up. Our politicians have let us down, and the nation has been denied a rational debate about the NHS. Most NHS consultants that I know regard the service as being in the red zone: there is little spare capacity and most services are running on empty. To quote Tudor Hart, back in 2006, 'We now need a new big picture, of where we have come from, where we want to go, and how we can get there.' I hope this book will provide useful insights to contribute to the debate on the future of health care in the UK as we seek to reverse years of decline and help to restore the NHS to its former glory.

Finally, an apology of sorts. I have tried to write a book that will resonate with other healthcare workers, whilst also being of interest more widely. Some might think that my perspective as a dermatologist limits the generalisability of what I have to say. They may be correct, but there is nothing about dermatology that makes it a special case. I have little doubt that the themes and events described in this book have been replicated elsewhere in the NHS and are just as relevant to rheumatology, colorectal surgery, cardiology and ophthalmology as they are to dermatology. No single author has the skills or experience to provide a coherent narrative about the whole of the UK's NHS; my apologies to anyone who thinks that this is what I have attempted to do. Perhaps a bigger text and multi-author format would have created something more reliable, objective and scholarly to tackle this enormous topic. Instead, you have my personal and opinionated ramblings. As someone who has devoted my working life to the NHS, and who still believes passionately in the concept, I hope that my views will not go unheeded. My ambition with this book is more modest than offering solutions; I just wanted to contribute to the debate that must now come if the NHS is to regain its position of pre-eminence.

Alex Anstey MD
30 September 2021
Alex.anstey@Doctors.org.uk

DEDICATION

I am most grateful to my sixth form critical readers from the Harris Federation in London. Your feedback humbled and inspired me; you were so positive and constructive about what I had written. I hereby dedicate this book to you, the fifteen 2021 UK medical school intake of the Harris Federation alumni: Amber at Imperial College School of Medicine; Philip at the University of St Andrews School of Medicine; Zainab, Lazo, Valerie and Christian at Brighton and Sussex Medical School; Eredia at St George's Hospital Medical School; Yesim and Rania at King's College London; Seir at Hull York Medical School; Heward at Queen Mary University of London; Gisel and Evvian at University of Exeter Medical School; Bradley at Kent and Medway Medical School; Louise at Lancaster Medical School.

FOREWORD

BY DR JULIA SCHOFIELD
AND PROFESSOR ANDREW FINLAY

This is an outstanding reflection on prevailing attitudes and possible solutions to the systemic failures of the NHS. It is also a great read, engaging, fast-paced and based around multiple short true-life stories. It is difficult to put down as Alex Anstey takes the reader at breakneck speed with him across his forty-year career, jumping from the present to the past to show how his work built on his previous experience. Anstey skilfully interweaves his own biography with fascinating historical insights and profiles of influential medical thinkers, explaining how these fused in his later career to inform and inspire his attempts to reshape one corner of the NHS. And he does not flinch from describing some of the emotional difficulties that he encountered and overcame, bringing the book further to life. Anstey is a succinct, clear and engaging writer, having spent years as a leading academic editor honing his skills.

Anstey's range of expertise and most importantly the novel thinking that he applied to his clinical work, teaching, research, administration and editorship is brilliantly explained in a way accessible to all. The reader is left somewhat exhausted by the sheer breadth of his achievements, but in great admiration of him and inspired to think more imaginatively about their own career and lives.

Anstey combines humanity and insight with a drive to understand, to pass on knowledge and to improve the patient's lot. He explains how the doctor establishing a closer relationship with a patient by itself helps that patient.

RESEARCH

Most clinical academics admit that they are unable to achieve at the highest level in all four of their key responsibilities, as clinician, teacher, researcher, and administrator, and tend to focus on one or two aspects, with perfunctory activity in the others. But not so with Anstey, who demonstrates a Renaissance Man attitude to his work and life, excelling across the board. We learn how Anstey recognised the importance of being involved in research at the very start of his career, and how he succeeded despite working in a department that did not support him. His early interests in two patients who developed severe drug reactions led him to publicise information about a test to identify those at risk and to lead international guidance over the use of that drug. This practical outcome, benefitting patients worldwide, was an excellent example of translational research, developing laboratory findings to enhance clinical practice. Later Anstey showed how focusing on a particular type of disease (e.g. skin conditions caused by or made worse by sunlight) can lead to further translational benefit, both for rare and common conditions.

Clinicians every week see a vast range of presentations of disease, but it takes an inquiring and prepared mind to recognise the really novel and potentially game changing cases. Meeting a profoundly affected child whose life was being ruined by his light-induced condition led to Anstey describing for the first time a previously ignored condition, and being able to help those affected. By mentoring and supervising younger clinical research-ers in the same areas of light-induced skin disease, Anstey was able to influence another generation of doctors in developing research skills as well as contributing to the scientific literature.

Anstey describes the difficulties in gaining funding for clinical research, and the imaginative ways that he has used to overcome these.

Integral to carrying out successful research is the ability to communicate the results, in other words to publish articles and publicise the work to researchers and clinicians. Anstey had become a clear and skilled writer before being appointed as editor of the *British Journal of Dermatology*, but his writing skills were clearly developed to a very high standard in his years as editor. The reader of this book benefits in every paragraph from Anstey's clarity, lack of verbosity and ability to hold the reader's interest. As editor Anstey transformed the *BJD*, creat-ing a huge international editorial team that has resulted in the *BJD* enhancing its prestige and value. Anstey was a transforma-tional editor, arguably the best *BJD* editor ever, though on this achievement at least he is remarkably modest.

NHS SERVICE CHANGE

Perhaps the most astonishing achievement related by Anstey is the dramatic increase in efficiency that he brought to his NHS clinical service, with no extra funding. His book describes the importance of putting patients at the centre of care and harnessing the knowledge and skills of all those involved in providing the service in order to make things work best for the patient.

His team approach is not just about including all those involved in providing the specialist service but demonstrates the powerful impact of breaking down the unhelpful barrier that exists between generalists (primary care clinicians) and specialists. Underpinned by the importance of recognising mutual respect for each other's skills, his creation of a cooperative integrated approach to skin disease management across primary and secondary care is now being used as an exemplar model across the NHS in England and Wales. The development of his specialist-led 'advice and guidance' model enables patients to receive high quality care from the appropriate health care worker at the right time. This story is too dramatic to ignore, and lessons must be learnt from Anstey's experience to inspire others to generate change and make a difference for myriads of other patients. Indeed, other centres who have independently developed a similar approach in response to the COVID-19 pandemic are reporting a similarly positive impact on waiting times.

It is all too easy for clinicians to accept long-held patterns of providing unsatisfactory models of clinical care, especially if for some there may be unacknowledged benefit in maintaining the status quo. Anstey's description of his ability to give as much importance to the non-medical members of his local team as to the great names in healthcare gives a very powerful message to the reader. He describes very clearly the benefit to patients of clinicians getting involved in service design and developing pragmatic local solutions for local problems. His description of all of these interactions, and the not entirely supportive reactions of other colleagues, provides a fascinating insight into the joys and hazards of provoking change.

TEACHING

As Anstey reminds us, it was Hippocrates who emphasised the responsibility that doctors have to teach others. And as with other aspects of his career, Anstey has never done things by halves. Enjoying teaching, he ensured that he became properly educated himself in teaching techniques, but then went on to take advantage of and further develop a range of new approaches to educating health professionals. He contributed to the transformation of dermatology nursing education in the UK by organising a national teaching/training programme. He set up a training course in photodermatology that complemented (and possibly overshadowed) an established national course. This was made more accessible by using novel distance learning techniques that involved his team creating a sound studio on a shoestring.

He created imaginative links with other disciplines. We learn how Anstey, by thinking and acting laterally, brought together the seemingly totally disparate disciplines of mathematical modelling and dermatology to create much greater efficiency in clinic organisation, as well as enhancing the education and career prospects of mathematics students.

He played a leading role in the organisation and delivery of medical student teaching in his university and contributed to the training of many junior skin specialists. His successful and well related attempts to inspire some students by taking them to visit the homes of Edward Jenner and William Osler illustrate his imaginative approach to his educational responsibilities. Another example of 'that's an excellent idea, why didn't I think of that?'

CONCLUSION

This is a once in a generation blending of biography, history, personal experience and suggestions for change: it may inspire similar efforts from others, but they are fated to be viewed as derivatives. It follows in the historical tradition of Mikhail Bulgakov's *A Country Doctor's Notebook*, Clement Gunn's *Leaves from the Life of a Country Doctor* and Mirna Situm's *Oranges and Dead Fish* in successfully letting the reader experience the realities of medical practice 'at the coalface', but offers much more besides. This book is strongly recommended to every medical student and junior doctor, but it is fascinating to anyone with a passing interest in the realities of clinical medicine and how the NHS might be improved. I wish that I had been able to read this book when I was a medical student or as a junior doctor. It would have been a great inspiration.

This is unique account of how the career of dermatology can be endlessly interesting and satisfying. It should be required reading for all dermatology trainees and is a great read for all medical students or junior doctors, or any doctor looking for inspiration. This book will contribute to influencing a generation of future dermatologists and make the competition to get into the specialty even fiercer.

JULIA SCHOFIELD

**Consultant Dermatologist, United Lincolnshire
Hospitals NHS Trust, Associate Professor, University of
Hertfordshire, Joint Clinical Lead, National Outpatient
Transformation Programme (NOTP)**

Julia grew up in Lincoln and trained in medicine in Manchester. Like Professor Anstey she completed GP training in Salford and for a while worked in primary care and dermatology before deciding to train as a consultant dermatologist. She completed dermatology training in Hertfordshire and the Royal London Hospital and was appointed as a consultant dermatologist in Hertfordshire in 1995. In 2006 she set up a master's programme in clinical dermatology at the University of Hertfordshire, which is the only multi-professional educational programme in dermatology of its type. The programme has been pivotal in the training and development of extended role practitioners, particularly nurse surgeons. A second very successful master's programme in skin lesion management was established in 2020. In 2008 Julia moved her NHS work to Lincolnshire, choosing to return to the town of her childhood to support her elderly parents.

Julia has been very much involved in service redesign since the early 2000s when she was clinical lead for the NHS Modernisation Agency Action on Dermatology and Plastic

Surgery programmes. She has worked closely with a broad range of stakeholders developing national guidance documents relating to service improvement in dermatology. More recently she has been seconded to NHSE&I as joint clinical lead for the National Outpatient Transformation programme where she was delighted to hear of Professor Anstey's exciting successful new model of care in North Wales. She is a trustee of the Psoriasis Association UK and was awarded an MBE for services to dermatology in 2012.

ANDREW FINLAY

**Professor of Dermatology, School of Medicine,
Cardiff University**

Andrew trained in medicine at St Mary's Hospital Medical
School, long before it was swallowed up by Imperial College.
He trained in general medicine around London before moving
to Cardiff to take advantage of the excellent dermatology
training there under Professor Ronnie Marks. He spent a year
at Mount Sinai Medical Centre, Miami Beach, and moved to
Glasgow for five years for his first post as consultant dermatologist. Moving back to Cardiff as senior lecturer, he was
eventually appointed professor of dermatology after Ronnie
retired. Andrew first met Alex Anstey when Alex also chose to
come to Cardiff for training, and worked with Alex in South
Wales over many years.

Andrew's service innovations included creating in Glasgow
one of the first integrated outpatient/inpatient dermatology
care centres. Responding to the still absurdly little dermatology
education required (or available) for general practice, he created
the international distance learning diploma in practical dermatology which over 4,000 GPs have successfully completed.

His main research interest has been in developing ways to
understand and measure the impact that skin diseases have on

people's lives. Several of the quality of life measures that his team created are now used worldwide, most notably the DLQI which is embedded in national guidelines and registries in over forty countries. His current research focus is on measuring the huge burden from the secondary impact of disease on patients' partners and family members, using the Family Reported Outcome Measure (FROM-16). He was appointed CBE in 2010.

'Why do we care so much? We care because
we feel that it is our duty to do so.'

Professor Donald Berwick

'I've got you under my skin. I've got you deep in
the heart of me. So deep in my heart that you're
really a part of me. I've got you under my skin'

Lyric by Cole Porter, as sung by Frank Sinatra

CHAPTER 1

A CLINIC ON
ITS KNEES

2017

I was having a bad day. I knew the clinic would be overbooked and running late, but as I made my way through the hospital corridors of Ysbyty Gwynedd, a district general hospital in North Wales, reflecting on the discussions at our morning management meeting, I wondered how things had got *this* bad. The busy clinic was symptomatic of the dangerously high level of demand. The dermatology patients shared a waiting area with cardiology and it was standing room only on this particular afternoon at 1:45 p.m. It had been raining all morning and the air was humid and stuffy. These clinics had a mixed demographic: poverty mixed with wealth, and a light sprinkling of UK and international students. All ages were represented too, from babies to the elderly and infirm. It would be a long afternoon.

'Pnawn da i chi!' ('Good afternoon to you!') I greeted the nurses and doctors who were milling around in the corridor outside the clinic rooms as I made my way to my room.

I logged onto the computer and loaded a fresh tape into my dictaphone. I glanced at the clinic list. There were six patients in the urgent suspected cancer category, four new urgent referrals, six new routine referrals and eight follow-up patients. Despite the computers on our desks and dermatoscopes (hand-held, illuminated magnification devices to permit high resolution imaging of the skin) in our hands, the ritual of the clinic had changed little in fifty years.

'Are you ready to start?' asked Mrs Hughes, my nurse for the afternoon.

'As ready as I ever will be. Who's first?'

She handed me a set of notes.

The first patient, a fifty-three-year-old woman, was shown in and sat next to me at my desk. She was anxious, having received an appointment on the urgent suspected cancer pathway. This is a fast track where patients are seen within two weeks of receipt of the GP referral. She was worried about a skin lesion on her back which had recently become itchy and sore. It turned out to be a benign skin lesion with no features to suggest skin cancer. Reassurance from me and smiles all round.

'I hope I haven't wasted your time, doctor?'

The next patient was a twenty-one-year-old university student with a long-standing mole on his arm. He was in cotton athletic clothing and had been soaked by the rain. His GP had spotted the mole when he was being seen for something else, and opted to refer him to have it checked. Again, he was attending within a few days of seeing his GP via the skin cancer fast track. There were no worrying or sinister features, and no suggestion of skin cancer. It was a small, benign birthmark. I checked it carefully with the dermatoscope and measured it with a ruler. Reassurance from me, but no smiles this time from a typically grumpy student whose breath smelt stale, perhaps still hungover from the night before.

The third patient was a woman of eighty-nine who attended with two of her daughters. They had travelled by car from Blaenau Ffestiniog, thirty-six miles away in the heart of Snowdonia. One daughter had taken the day off work; the other was not working, but came anyway. This was a referral to check multiple pigmented lesions on her back. Again, she had been referred by her GP on the skin cancer fast track. I took my time, respectful and solicitous to this elderly woman.

'Her first language is Welsh, and her English is a bit rusty,' one daughter told me. '...And she's getting a bit forgetful,' added the other.

I carefully checked the skin on her back and chest. There were multiple black and brown pigmented lesions, all show-ing the typical features of seborrhoeic keratoses, or 'age spots'. Again, it was reassurance and smiles. However, this time they did not get up to leave. 'While we're here, doctor...' I duly checked the second skin problem, a mild form of eczema seen in the elderly, where the outer layers of the skin become dry and cracked creating a lattice-like pattern of eczema on the legs. I wrote a prescription for a moisturising cream and a moderately potent steroid cream.

'Diolch yn fawr iawn,' a daughter said as they were leaving (thank you very much).

And so it went on. Patient after patient with not too much wrong with them. Nice in a way, but frustrating too. These cases should never have been fast-tracked to the head of the queue, but that was how the system was set up. The GPs who had referred them were doing their best with their limited knowledge and even more limited training. They were terrified of missing something serious, and were practicing what's commonly referred to as defensive medicine. How British to be concerned about wasting my time, how typical of NHS patients.

Perhaps they did not recognise that their appointment had consumed far more of their time than mine: the half day travelling to the hospital; the time spent driving round and round searching for a parking place; walking from their car to the outpatient department; queuing to be checked into the clinic; waiting in the waiting room; being seen by the doctor; walking back to their car; driving home. For me it was just a few minutes in the clinic.

'Better safe than sorry,' I did my best to reassure them, and confirm that it was always best to check these things if they or their GP were concerned.

The next patient, Rhiannon, a fifteen-year-old girl with bad acne, was being teased at school. She attended with her mother and they had travelled about twenty-five miles from Holyhead. Rhiannon had been on antibiotics for nearly three years. They had waited patiently for this appointment; despite me upgrading from 'routine' to 'urgent' on reading the referral letter it was still a four-month wait (a routine appointment would have involved a twelve-month wait). I examined her skin, trying to conceal my concern. I could see that this was severe inflammatory acne with scarring, visible through the thickly applied make-up. The treatment I was planning would be a game-changer. If Rhiannon had been referred earlier, there would likely have been less scarring. I tried to be upbeat and positive as I explained about the benefits of Roaccutane.

Next up was Meinir, a twenty-three-year-old with psoriasis. It was involving her scalp, elbows, knees and genital skin. I asked her to complete a ten-item quality of life questionnaire. Her score was much higher than I was expecting, telling me that her skin disease was having a big impact on her quality of life.

'What is the main issue?' I asked

'It is too painful and embarrassing to have sex,' she replied.

I looked at the priority and date of her GP referral letter: 'routine', but then upgraded by me to 'urgent'. She too had waited four months to be seen. Meinir had considered going private, but couldn't afford it.

The next patient had been added as an 'extra'. The GP had phoned me a few days earlier, and had threatened to send the patient in for admission to a medical ward. I agreed to see him in clinic later in the same week. Gwion was aged seventeen, and had suffered with eczema since infancy. He had been seen by us a couple of times in the past, yet still had very little idea about how to self-manage his eczema. It was now dominating his life, always itchy, always distressing, and stopping him from sleeping. He scratched his skin vigorously throughout the consultation, even when talking to me and whilst I examined his skin. There was no respite.

'How does it feel to scratch your skin like that?' I said

He looked surprised by the question. Eye contact told him I already knew the answer. He realised that lying would be pointless.

'Actually... it feels great! It's the best feeling ever, but I know I shouldn't do it. If I keep going, I end up in a frenzy and scratch myself harder and harder until my skin bleeds. It still feels nice to scratch, even then.' A nod of recognition from me, to acknowledge that I fully understood what he was saying, without being judgemental or critical.

Nearing the end of the clinic, it was time to see the review patients, all of whom I knew. I apologised to each in turn for the clinic running so late. They were used to it; this clinic always ran late. They knew it and tried not to get too stressed. However, most of these patients had severe and complex skin diseases, requiring treatment with potent drugs targeted at the immune system. This was hardly the best way to treat our most needy and vulnerable patients. It felt too rushed making decisions that were hasty and expedient rather than appropriate and well-considered.

The first follow-up had a rare autoimmune blistering disease (a disease where the body's immune system attacks the skin and creates inflammation and blisters) which had failed to respond to dapsone, the drug of first choice. There were now three different treatment options to consider, which meant delaying a decision until the patient had a chance to read the relevant patient information leaflets, and give it some thought. However, he wanted to avoid another clinic appointment and was keen to start something today. I knew that this was reverting back to paternalistic medicine, with me making the decisions, and the patient trusting my judgement. He seemed to have made up his mind, so I went along with his wishes and started him on a new tablet.

Next in was a patient who had recently started a new therapy for his bad psoriasis. He had completed sixteen weeks of treatment with adalimumab via self-administered injections to the anterior thigh or tummy, once every two weeks.

'How is it going?' I said as he came in and sat down.

'Brilliant,' he said. 'It's all cleared up.'

'Any side effects or problems?'

'No. The injections sting a bit, but I can cope with that.'

He stripped off in the examination room so I could see his skin for myself. He had a tiny area of psoriasis on his left shin, but was otherwise clear. I had never seen his skin normal-looking like this. He completed the quality of life questionnaire. I informed him that he was now eligible for long-term treatment with this drug. He went out smiling, no longer handicapped by bad skin disease.

Next in was a female patient of thirty-one years with bad eczema. She had recently started an immune-suppressant drug in the hope of improving her symptoms. I knew her well, having seen her in clinic on many occasions.

'How's it going, Rachel?' I asked.

'I couldn't cope with those capsules. You warned me about their funny smell and huge size; I could just about swallow them without gagging. However, a few hours after starting them I developed a thumping headache. I stopped them and tried again a few days later. Again, I woke the next day with a bad headache. So, I stopped taking them. My eczema is still awful.'

We discussed the treatment options. I told Rachel about dupilumab, a new injection for eczema which had recently become available. I explained that these were self-administered injections, every two weeks. They were very effective and safe, with a low incidence of side effects. I explained how she could obtain more information, and we agreed to meet again in two weeks to discuss it in more detail. She was visibly relieved to be leaving the clinic with a plan, and seemed excited to be considering a novel new treatment.

At the end of the clinic were patients from the end of the 'routine' waiting list.

The first patient had been waiting for twelve months (more than twelve months means they would breach the waiting list limits set by Wales NHS; our service ran at the limits); in frustration, he had been to see a dermatologist privately. The problem had been sorted out, but he now had another skin problem, so had decided to keep the appointment anyway.

And there was the patient with a skin disease which had lasted for a few months, but was now better. He kept the appointment to seek advice on what he should do if the rash came back.

There was also the thirty-seven-year-old woman with a mole on her face which was unsightly. The GP had said in the referral letter that it had changed slightly in appearance; by the time she attended clinic twelve months later she forgot to mention this; the only issue was to have it removed because she felt that it was ugly.

I apologised: 'We are not allowed to do procedures for cosmetic reasons.'

'Then why did you make me wait more than a year to be seen?' she asked.

It was a good question. She had waited for twelve months, and taken a day off work to attend this appointment, only to find out something she could have been told at the outset. She argued strongly to have it done, but I stuck to the line. She left in a huff, slamming the door behind her.

And finally, the patient with a skin lesion the GP thought was benign, but wanted it looked at anyway. Again, it had been a twelve-month wait for this fifty-five-year-old woman on the routine waiting list. In that time, the lesion had slowly changed in appearance, becoming larger and more irregular. She was a busy, cheerful, outgoing woman, who had made light of this lesion. I examined it with my dermatoscope, fearing the worst. Sure enough, there were a number of worrying features. I suspected a malignant melanoma, a serious form of skin cancer which kills more than 6,000 people per year in the UK. I explained what I thought was the diagnosis, and made arrangements for excision of this lesion a few days later.

●　　●　　●

Clinic over, I drove through the landscape which plunges into the sea between Bangor and Llandudno. The road clung precariously to the side of the mountains before disappearing into long brightly lit tunnels, giving me time to reflect on my day. The service we were providing was a shambles. Why did managers think that by just about coping with the high volume of referrals, with no breaches, we were providing a good quality service? Just because the waiting times had not breached the stipulated maximum wait permitted in national waiting list targets did not mean there wasn't a crisis. Nor was there any talk of how we might improve the service. I hated this acceptance of a poorly performing service. I was sure we could do better.

'How was your day?' said my wife, Sarah, that evening at supper. She could see there was something on my mind.

'Our dermatology service is failing, but no one seems concerned about it. One of the managers even said to me, "It has always been like this," and shrugged.'

Then I told Sarah about the afternoon clinic.

'That bad, eh?' she said. 'So *do* something about it.'

I slept badly for the next few nights as I mulled over our situation.

The poor lady with a suspected melanoma who had been hidden in plain sight on our routine waiting list for the last twelve months was just the tip of the iceberg.

Enough was enough.

•　　•　　•

A few weeks later, I set myself a challenge. A big part of the problem was that our interactions with the GPs were so poor. Almost exclusively by letter, these referrals and responses typically took weeks or months even for a single exchange of letters. In every department I'd worked in, the system was the same.

Referral letters from GPs were divided by consultants according to three categories: 'urgent suspected cancers'; 'urgent'; 'routine'.

This created three large piles of letters.

I had never questioned this; it had been a constant throughout my career. However, as our service was clearly failing, I needed to give it more thought.

The next question was about the old-style three-category prioritisation process: how did this work in practice for the patients in each group?

My diary entry for that day was:

Started with 'urgent suspected cancers' (USC). Looked through the USC referrals, each on the characteristic yellow paper we used to make them stand out from more mundane referrals. Only three out of eighteen had been correctly referred on this pathway. Worse than expected! However, not necessarily the fault of the GPs; few of them have had proper training in skin cancer recognition.

This clinical pathway is failing badly.

Next, I looked at urgent referrals. Bigger pile of referral letters than expected with fifteen letters. Included small but significant number of serious skin cancers where the GP should have used the 'urgent suspected cancer' pathway. This creates a significant patient risk; these patients are waiting for four months or longer to be seen, instead of two weeks via the skin cancer pathway. Most referrals in the urgent pile included patients correctly prioritised by GPs (no concerns about this). However, our capacity to see these patients is far too low. Upshot? Four months for an appointment. Again, pretty poor. GPs tell me that they try to manage these patients, knowing that with such long waiting lists, there is no other choice. I was trying to imagine how the GPs feel when the hospital responds to their legitimate urgent referral with a four-month wait. Four months for parents of babies with terrible infantile eczema! Four months for teenagers with severe, scarring acne! Four months for someone with severe psoriasis! Yes, urgent category also a dismal failure.

Slightly dreading what I would find in the 'routine' referrals. I found patients currently waiting for between twelve and fourteen months for an appointment. It was clear that most were patients with significant skin complaints. It emphasised that 'routine' did not mean 'trivial'. Deciding to dig deeper, I spoke to Kerrie Gallear, dermatology clinic clerk. I asked her to show me the whole of the routine waiting list. She looked surprised; no consultant had previously shown an interest in this group of patients. I caught her eyes flicking nervously to the top shelf above her desk, and then back to me.

'No? Surely not?' I said.

'Afraid so,' she replied.

The whole of the top shelf was occupied by thirteen thick ring binders, each containing about a hundred referral letters, arranged in date order, the newest on the left, the oldest on the right.

We counted: there were 1,350 patients on our routine waiting list. The wait to be seen was over twelve months.

It was clear to both of us that the system was failing.

No category of patient referral was working well. The patients were getting a raw deal. The government wasn't about to, but how could we change what we were doing?

And then I had written, '*What would Betsi do?*'

CHAPTER 2

BETSI CADWALADR, MEDICAL HERO

1789-1860

Betsi Cadwaladr, our legendary health board figurehead, came to nursing late in life, having travelled the world as a ship's steward. On board ship in the early 1800s, her duties involved caring for the paying passengers. These voyages took Betsi to Australia and Tasmania, India and South America. Five days after the Battle of Waterloo (18 June 1815), Betsi found the battlefield still covered with bodies. The sight of these dead soldiers and the people searching them for friends and family, as well as human scavengers and carrion, left a lasting impression on Betsi. It was probably then that she determined to become a nurse, and care for her fellow human beings.

Over thirty years later, in her sixties, Betsi sought to consolidate her knowledge of nursing by training at Guy's Hospital, in preparation for a more sedate life as a private nurse. In the autumn of 1854 Betsi was between nursing jobs and staying with her sister Bridget in London when she came across an article in *The Times* that would change her life. It described the Battle of the Alma, the opening encounter in the Crimean War with Russia. William H. Russell was making quite a name for himself as a war correspondent; this was the first overseas war to be reported to the citizens of the United Kingdom. Betsi was transported by the vividness of the reporting, perhaps reminded of the aftermath of the Battle of Waterloo. She responded to a plea in *The Times* for nurses to care for 'our men' in the Crimea. Although the allies had prevailed at the Alma, the cost had been high. This confirmed that volunteering for nursing duties was Betsi's true calling. She joined the first cohort that was sent out. Her arrival there, along with thirty-seven other nurses, was reported by Russell in *The Times*:

'With an incredible amount of hard work, the nurses in Nightingale's charge brought the Scutari Hospital into better order and 46 more nurses had arrived in Crimea by December. Despite a rise in the number of nurses the workload was overwhelming. At one point less than 100 nurses had 10,000 men under their care. By February 1855 the death rate was running at 42%.'

Betsi was clearly frustrated at being subordinate to the much younger Florence Nightingale. Florence had taken charge of Selimiye Barrack Hospital in Scutari, Istanbul. Betsi felt that her talents were being wasted, far from the battlefront where the greatest concentration of casualties and injured were located. Having travelled so far, she was now in Turkey, still remote from the action on the other side of the Black Sea, and doing what she regarded as menial work. She was determined to prevail and forced the issue by insisting on going to the front-line hospital at Balaclava, nearly 300 miles away, on the Crimean Peninsula. Florence said that she could go, but they parted on frosty terms. 'If you misbehave yourself,' Florence threatened, 'there will be no home for you here, and you will be sent straight to England from the Crimea.' Betsi was indignant at this slight to her good name and character, feeling that Florence was treating her 'like a dog'. Florence agreed to her request, and facilitated Betsi's onward travel to Balaclava. However, she also had made it clear that she would not accept any responsibility for Betsi if she went.

Arriving in Balaclava Barrack Hospital a few days later, Betsi was shocked by what she found: soldiers with foul wounds teeming with maggots; men with frostbite and gangrene; no beds for the sick who lay upon boards; greatcoats instead of pillows; patients unclean, smelly and neglected; wards over-run by vermin; occasional meals for the sick, many of whom were starving. Worse still was the discovery that everything needed to address these shortcomings was locked up in the stores; most of this suffering and neglect was unnecessary and avoidable. Betsi's instincts had been correct; this was exactly what she was seeking. A place that desperately needed what she had to offer.

Betsi Cadwaladr and Florence Nightingale came from opposite ends of the social spectrum. While Florence was privileged, wealthy and well connected, Betsi was underprivileged, making do with whatever she had, and relying on common sense, hard work and her own moral compass rather than on connections. Florence followed the rules meticulously, collected data and even used statistics to analyse performance and come up with solutions. In contrast, Betsi was intuitive, guided by her heart and natural instincts. Her actions were informed by years of experience, pragmatism, common sense and honesty.

When necessary, Betsi would bend the rules, but not for personal gain. She was creative in finding solutions when faced with limited resources. For example, Betsi discovered that the military stores and supply chain regulations were overly restrictive and sometimes nonsensical. Meanwhile, the men she and the other nurses were caring for were starving on their subsistence rations. Betsi made common purpose with the army supplies team at Balaclava, making it clear that she would not take no for an answer. She reorganised the kitchens at the hospital, and was soon making flavoursome and nutritious food in sufficient quantities for the wounded and dying men. Her experience at cooking and running the galley and making the best use of supplies in ocean-going ships for the previous thirty years was crucial; without this expertise, many of these men would have starved. She and her nurses cleaned the wards, replaced the trestle and board bunks with beds, mattresses and clean bedding. They cleansed and dressed the soldier's wounds, washed their bodies, and combed their hair. Old clothing was replaced with new. The nurses made the beds and the orderlies helped the men into them. They were now well fed and cared for with kindness and compassion, in wards which were cleaner than they had been. It was rough around the edges, but the results spoke for themselves, as Florence Nightingale grudgingly acknowledged when she finally visited the hospital at Balaclava six months later.

Although Betsi and Florence could not be described as friends, they acquired a mutual respect for each other, perhaps recognising their bonds of gender and service in this most challenging of environments. It was now clear to both that there was no question of Betsi 'misbehaving herself'; Florence must have realised that she had previously misjudged Betsi, and had been unfair to this enterprising and resourceful working-class woman from Wales. A grateful patient, an officer, writing to the nursing superintendent at Balaclava having recovered and returned to his native Sardinia, referred to Betsi (using the adopted name of Davis; few could pronounce Cadwaladr):

'I hope Davis is well. She is ever to be depended on, good, honest and devoted.'

Betsi described her work and the work of the other nurses in Balaclava as follows: 'All ranks and of all nations, were equally cared for, and nursed with unremitting attention, and impartial kindness.'

Most touching of all was the testimonial in Betsi's autobiography from Margaret Wear, her friend and supervisor at Balaclava: 'I cannot hope to find anyone who will do all you have done so long, so untiring, and often where all others equally ill would have remained in bed; for never, for one single day, during six months in this climate, and in the pestilential air of this hospital did you ever desert your post: up early and late, and ever preparing comforts for between two and three hundred sick!'

Betsi then became sick with cholera and dysentery. She opted to go home to recover, perhaps sensing that to stay was to risk death. She was now aged sixty-five and recognised that her travels and adventures were coming to an end. She now had a deep longing for home, *hiraeth* in Welsh. Florence Nightingale granted her wish and organised the travel arrangements. Betsi survived the journey home, and was nursed back to health by her sister Bridget, in London. In her convalescence, Betsi shared her stories with fellow Welsh woman and scholar Jane Williams. Ms Williams quickly recognised the uniqueness and interest of Betsi's stories, and their historical significance. Betsi agreed to have her memoirs recorded for publication, with Jane Williams as her ghostwriter and editor. The book was published in 1857, three years before Betsi died in 1860.

•   •   •

A few months after that memorably bad clinic in 2017, I visited Betsi's childhood home. When I had asked colleagues and friends what they knew about Betsi, I was greeted with blank stares and complaints about her tongue-twister of a name. A few referred to her as 'the Welsh Florence Nightingale', but this was still wide of the mark. I was intrigued. I did some background reading, and set off with Moli, our cockerpoo, to explore Bala on our own Betsi Cadwaladr Heritage Trail.

Betsi's family home was Pen Rhiw Farm in the parish of Llanycil. The farm was easy to find, down a muddy track with a sign showing the farm's name. The primroses and gorse were flowering, a sure sign that spring was coming. I was searching for a rock in a field close to the farm which had a cavernous hole or hollow that Betsi used as her private place of retreat at times of sibling strife. It must be hidden from the house, I thought, or Betsi would have been spotted by her siblings. We walked in a circle around the farmhouse, keeping to rights of way when possible, and looking carefully at the free-standing stones and rocky outcrops for Betsi's juvenile hiding place. Stopping to catch our breath, we admired the view. To the west was the mountain Aran Benllyn, sloping up and away from Llyn Tegid, the Welsh name for Bala Lake. We were overlooking Pen Rhiw Farm about a mile distant. I tried to imagine what life had been like for Betsi, her parents and her fifteen siblings. Their father, Dafydd Cadwalady, a preacher to Welsh Calvinistic Methodists, walked for miles, and was often away for days, leaving his wife, Betsi's mother, Judith Erasmus, to hold the fort. Although an idyllic place on this bright morning in late March, I tried to imagine life in this small, isolated farmhouse, with Dafydd out preaching most of the time. I wondered who did the farming whilst Dafydd was away.

The story goes that on one occasion, Dafydd's Welsh bible was nearly confiscated and destroyed by a local Justice as he had forgotten to carry his Licence to Preach. He pleaded his case so passionately that the Justice was eventually persuaded. Dafydd was released and allowed to keep his Welsh bible. This story has added poignancy, having taken place at Capel Curig, just a few miles from Ty Mawr (literally 'Big House'), the birthplace and family home of William Morgan. For it was the scholarly Morgan who had learnt Hebrew so that he could translate the bible direct from the source into Welsh, without English as a stepping stone; perhaps the single most important contribution to preserving the Welsh language, and creating the shared identity of the Welsh nation for subsequent generations. Betsi strongly identified herself as Welsh, and bore this with great pride. Her self-image and values had been created in the Welsh language, the Welsh bible having a central role. Betsi's falling-out with Florence Nightingale was partly on account of Florence's failure to recognise the identity and values of this working-class Welsh woman.

We drove in to Bala, and saw the school, rebuilt and modernised since Betsi's day, but still in the same location. Having lost her mother aged five, Betsi was bullied by her older sister, on whom it now fell to take charge of the little ones. At the age of nine, Betsi invited herself to live with her father's landlord and his wife, the Lloyds, at Plas yn Dref on Bala high street, just a couple of miles from the Cadwalady farmhouse. Mr and Mrs Lloyd were surprised to receive this application from Betsi. However, they took it seriously and discussed it with Dafydd Cadwalady, who agreed that Betsi could stay and 'learn to be useful'. She stayed for five years, treated as a family member, until, aged fourteen, she ran away again, sneaking out of Plas yn Dref at night, her few clothes and possessions tied in a bundle.

She set off for Liverpool, intent on seeing the world and making something of herself.

Plas yn Dref was easily found, now a pub with rooms and a restaurant, where I was served a delicious ham sandwich, my dog Moli allowed to sit beneath the table. I reflected on Betsi's remarkable survival skills. In Liverpool, a booming port town soon set to rival London, she found work as a domestic servant before taking positions on ships sailing to Europe. Reluctant to give up her independence, she turned down multiple proposals of marriage and instead started working on larger sailing ships, first to the West Indies, and then Australia. She was put in charge of letting berths, making arrangements for the passengers, and managing the stores. She coordinated the kitchens during the voyages, and cared for the passengers if needed. Her duties including midwifery.

I knew that Betsi had been a nurse at Balaclava soon after the Charge of the Light Brigade, a spectacularly failed military action, with confusing messages resulting in lightly armed cavalry charging heavy military guns. There were few survivors. Betsi may have come across one of the soldiers who returned from the 'Valley of Death', a young Welsh officer by the name of Captain Godfrey Morgan. Godfrey would later play a key role in creating the very hospitals in South East Wales from which the concept of the NHS germinated. He would certainly have visited his wounded men, who were cared for by Betsi and her fellow nurses. Maybe this enlightened young officer witnessed the transformation in Balaclava Hospital, as it changed from a hell in which to die, to somewhere where recovery was possible for the sick and wounded. Did Godfrey see for himself the role Betsi played in this transformation?

As I drove home from Bala on that early spring day in 2018, I tried to imagine Betsi today.

What would Betsi do, faced with my failing dermatology service?

Balaclava Hospital, Crimea

Now that I had come to know Betsi better, the answer was obvious.

She would have rolled up her sleeves and sorted it out.

What was I waiting for?

• • •

MALE, SEVENTY-EIGHT, SKIN LYMPHOMA

He is an elderly man and lives alone. He suffers from a chronic skin disorder, and has attended a few times. I ask him how he fills his days. 'Oh, the usual... shopping... cleaning... cooking... clearing up.' 'Yes, but what do you do that you really enjoy?' 'I collect stamps.' 'Which is your best stamp?' ...and so it went on. The next time he came to clinic, he brought along some stamps to show me. I call in Nia Williams, the clinic nurse, and we look through his display books together. His whole demeanour has changed, with a sparkle in his eye, and a different tone to his voice; we have hit his sweet spot. When he attends my clinic now, I take one look at him and think 'stamps', and his whole story comes back to me, including the details of his skin condition.

CHAPTER 3

INTEGRATING CARE?

2018-2019

After six years, I was stepping down as editor of the *British Journal of Dermatology*. It had been an exhilarating but bumpy experience, like flying a plane through a prolonged spell of bad weather and finally emerging into the sunshine. I now needed to find something else to focus on.

'What are you going to do now?' was the question that came up repeatedly.

Remembering Betsi, I said, 'Make the NHS work.'

'Ha, good luck with that.' My comment always generated a laugh, raised eyebrows, or a 'Crikey-is-that-the-time' bid for freedom.

But I was serious in my ambition and hopeful that I could pull it off. I had been thinking about it for years; this was my first time as clinical director, the consultant in overall charge of the local dermatology service. With the position came a once in a lifetime opportunity to put theory into practice.

My overall impression of working as a consultant dermatologist for twenty-five years in the UK's National Health Service was that we could do better.

In other words, it was possible to improve the service for patients with skin disease in my local patch of the NHS in North West Wales: Anglesey, Gwynedd and Conwy, with thirty-five GP surgeries, 230 GPs and a population of 250,000.

We had moved to North Wales in 2015 to be nearer to my wife's family around Wrexham and Chester. We knew it to be an area of outstanding natural beauty from our regular family holidays on the Llŷn Peninsula. The consultant dermatologists in North Wales had encouraged me to join them.

Here I need to introduce Dr Steve MacVicar, a GP in Beaumaris on Anglesey. Steve was the local lead for primary care. In 2017 I had asked to meet him in order to discuss a new way of running dermatology services that I was considering. He sounded interested, and we agreed to meet a few weeks later in my office at Ysbyty Gwynedd.

Steve was softly spoken and engaging, someone who listened carefully before giving an answer. We struck up a friendship as we analysed the long-standing problems with dermatology services in this part of North Wales. My idea was to place greater emphasis on collaborative care for patients with skin diseases, the specialist and GP teams working closely together. If most of the work could be retained upstream with primary care, there was a chance that hospital care downstream could be rescued from the deluge of patients. In other words, I wanted to break down the sterile divide that separated specialist and GP teams. We agreed that this old system was failing badly, as illustrated by the unacceptably long waiting lists. I explained to Steve that my colleague Dr Andy Macfarlane was soon retiring, and I would then be single-handed; this would be a good moment to change the way we worked.

We discussed the new way of working: a system that would be rapidly responsive, with speedy patient access to the specialist team when needed. This new system must work for the GPs who required guidance and support as they took on the care of patients with skin disease in the community. To do this, GPs needed quick access to specialist advice. In essence, the new way of working included three simple changes: first, for GPs to include photographs of the skin with their referral letters; secondly, acceptance that many referrals could be dealt with by timely advice and guidance from the specialist without the need to attend hospital for an outpatient appointment; thirdly, the specialist team and GPs should meet regularly, to share stories, listen to each other, and learn together. With thirty-five GP practices in the area, and nearly 230 GPs, this required a rolling programme of meetings between the specialist and GP teams. In essence, I was proposing that we create one new integrated team consisting of specialists (the hospital doctors) and generalists (the GPs). We would call this new model 'Dermatology Integrated Care'.

Steve liked my idea and felt that it might work. In 2018 we tested the concept on a limited basis on the island of Anglesey, which included his own practice in Beaumaris. Steve contacted the local GPs in the eleven practices on Anglesey; they agreed to run with the proposal. Early signs were positive, but a few months later Steve retired from the NHS; I had to start again with a new lead for primary care. I need not have worried. Dr Bethan Jones, Steve's replacement, was even more positive about my ideas to change the system. Bethan was a GP at Bron Derw, a large teaching practice in Bangor, and was now employed by the health board for two days each week as the medical director for primary care. My time as journal editor was nearly over; I was ready for this fresh challenge.

In late 2018, Bethan and I announced the new model of care for dermatology services across Anglesey, Gwynedd and Conwy, a catchment population of 250,000. Bethan contacted all thirty-five of the GP practices to explain the new concept; there were no dissenting voices. The GPs were supportive and Dermatology Integrated Care was launched. The team included senior pharmacist Alaw Jones, appointed to create a more rational and prudent approach to prescribing high-cost medications. Where alternative drugs were available, we discussed cheaper treatments with patients, being clear about why we were doing this; patients could revert to the more costly drug if the cheaper drug was less effective or poorly tolerated. Interestingly, most patients embraced this idea, pleased to do their bit for the NHS. We saved £125,000 in just twelve months from the previously overspent drug budget, a reduction of 22 per cent, reversing the previous year-on-year 10–15 per cent increase for dermatology drug spend. The managers were delighted; having made big savings, we could now start much-needed investment in the service.

Dermatology services in our sector of the health board (West) were performing well compared to the rest of the health board. We realised this new model of care needed to be shared with dermatology colleagues working in the two other areas of the health board: Central and East. We created a document which described what we had done, and shared it by email with the rest of the dermatology team: three consultant dermatologists in Central and four in East. Our NHS managers were excited about what we were doing in West; everyone seemed to be talking about it.

I was asked by Sue Wood, a senior nurse turned NHS manager, to do a presentation to a new online Welsh Government health forum. Sue was now the health board representative for NHS Wales for outpatient services and was keen to share best practice across the principality. The format was simple: Welsh Government hosted the forum, and participants joined online. I was in Bangor with Eleri Roberts, our dermatology manager, and Dr Bethan Jones, medical director for primary care in our area. These two had been my partners in developing and introducing Dermatology Integrated Care. This was only the second 'Best Practice Carousel' webinar hosted by Welsh Government, and the first involving our health board. It wasn't surprising that we felt a sense of anxious anticipation, the three of us positive about our success, and keen to share our model of care with our healthcare colleagues.

Seventeen centres from across Wales joined us, from Aberystwyth to Abergavenny, Barry to Bangor. I described Dermatology Integrated Care and highlighted how it differed from the old way of working, using performance graphs to show the dramatically reduced dermatology waiting lists in our area. Alaw Jones, our senior pharmacist, supplied me with data on pharmacy spend for dermatology across the health board; these showed the savings for our area of £125,000 in twelve months, whilst pharmacy spending elsewhere in the health board for dermatology had increased. Dr Bethan Jones explained how positive the local GPs were about Dermatology Integrated Care, and said that patients and GPs appreciated the speedier access to care. Bethan said that patients from her practice liked the new system, particularly receiving personalised advice and guidance letters so soon after the initial referral; this was much preferred to the old way of working with a long wait for a hospital appointment and complete silence in the interim period.

There was lively discussion and lots of useful comments. I was asked if Dermatology Integrated Care would be adopted by the rest of our health board and elsewhere in Wales.

'I'm more than willing to help others adopt our system,' I said.

To be honest, I had mixed feelings. On the one hand I was delighted that Dermatology Integrated Care was working so well and proud to share it with others; on the other hand, I was apprehensive about the silence from my dermatology colleagues regarding our service change. I knew that elsewhere in the health board, dermatology services had yet to undergo a similar process of modernisation and change; they were beset by multiple service delivery issues and still had long waiting lists. As I drove home that night from work, I was reminded of how poorly prepared I had been for a career in medicine by medical school training, and how ill-served I had been for life in the real world by private education. It now felt good to look back on my early life from the position of leader of a successful healthcare team. I was at ease with myself, proud of my team, optimistic and fulfilled by our collective positive impact on patient care.

CHAPTER 4

PRE-MED

1959-1983

I was born in Westerham, Kent in January 1959, delivered at home by my father Richard as the midwife failed to make it. We lived in the last house on Hosey Hill, just one mile from Chartwell, the former home of Winston Churchill. My mother Denyse was born in South Africa to a French family. She had arrived in the UK in her early twenties with little money, a South African accent and a love of classical music. Richard wasn't bothered about accents, having grown up in a family with a cook, a butler and an assumption that one went to Eton (as his father had done); it had put him off posh accents for life. He too was passionate about classical music.

I was the third of four children; there was also a large extended family with numerous uncles, aunts and cousins. Our home was a happy but noisy place, with Richard often using his hi-fi to drown out the shouts and screams of the children. My parents were naturists too; all very embarrassing when I had friends to stay. At the age of thirteen, my parents announced that I would be going to school at Eton. This seemed like a random idea, as I was completely unprepared for schooling of this type. The school were clearly impressed by my common entrance exam papers where I stated that I was applying to Eaten Collage (spelling was never a strong point). I survived Eton, but was determined to take a career path with as few Old Etonians as possible: medicine beckoned. I scraped into a London medical school.

The year before Mrs Thatcher entered Number 10, I began my medical journey at Charing Cross Hospital Medical School in London. The news backdrop to that September in 1978 was inauspicious, dominated by a medical story. Just as the World Health Organisation was about to declare smallpox eradicated, there was an unexpected outbreak in Birmingham. A medical photographer at Birmingham University Medical School, Janet Parker, became unwell with a striking rash; it was smallpox. The diagnosis was confirmed by the head of the microbiology laboratory that had been the source of the virus (Janet Parker's darkroom was immediately above the microbiology laboratory). Parker's was the very last death in the world from this disease. Just a year earlier, the World Health Organisation had rejected an application from this Birmingham research laboratory to partici-pate in ongoing smallpox research, mainly due to safety concerns; despite this, the research had continued. Tragically, the head of the laboratory also died as a result of this outbreak, slashing his own throat in his garden shed and dying a few days later. The subsequent official report led by RA Shooter, a microbiologist, was one of the most damning ever produced by an enquiry in the UK. Shooter's report has contemporary resonance, too – the World Health Organisation is still uncertain about the source of

COVID-19, and a laboratory leak from the Wuhan Institute of Virology has still not been completely ruled out.

Despite the drama of this medical story, at the time I was more interested in reading the back pages of the newspapers: QPR were London's top football team; Chelsea had gone bust whilst *boring* Arsenal specialised in winning 1:0; Spurs were exotic and modestly successful; Liverpool played with passion. The England football team and Nottingham Forest FC taught us the importance of teamwork: England by demonstrating what happens without it; Forest by demonstrating what can be achieved with it. Then something happened that ushered in a profound cultural shift in social norms and our value system. For the first time in British history, footballers started earning more than teachers. Everything was starting to change, and was up for grabs. Traditional, uptight, class-ridden, stiff-upper-lip Britain seemed poorly prepared for the series of shocks and disasters that would punctuate life in the UK over the next few decades. Little did we realise at the time that damning reports, like Shooter's, would soon become the norm, reflective commentaries on the events that they described.

In addition to seeing some great football, student life in London was also notable for live music. The soundtrack at this time included some of the finest bands of the era, Bob Marley, David Bowie, The Who, Miles Davies, Johnny Rotten, Talking Heads, The Clash, Led Zeppelin and Prince. It would also feature the strident cadences of Margaret Thatcher. Mrs Thatcher took on the unions in a way that her predecessors had avoided. Her dogma, ideology and lack of empathy for those who suffered under the huge cuts in public spending set the tone for a certain type of politics that reshaped the British land-scape. The steel-making, coal mining, car manufacturing and ship-building industries were sold off, massively reduced in size or closed down altogether. Arthur Scargill, president of the National Union of Mineworkers, was regularly on the TV news, berating Mrs Thatcher and urging the miners on. He met his match in Margaret Thatcher. Unlike today's government with their weekly U-turns, Mrs Thatcher held her ground.

'You turn if you want to. The lady's not for turning.'

The voters lapped it up and the Tories prevailed. Although many tried to challenge Mrs Thatcher during this era, none exalted in doing this more than Bjørge Lillelien, a Norwegian football commentator, in September 1981: 'We have beaten England! England, birthplace of giants. Lord Nelson, Lord Beaverbrook, Sir Winston Churchill, Sir Anthony Eden, Clement Attlee, Henry Cooper, Lady Diana. We have beaten them all. Maggie Thatcher, can you hear me? Maggie Thatcher, I have a message for you in the middle of an election campaign. Your boys took a hell of a beating!'

As graduates in 1983, we were bursting with hope and idealism. What we would come to realise, however, was that our medical school training had overlooked the need to prepare us as compassionate, socially aware and skilled doctors. Bedside manner was not on the curriculum. The idea was that by cram-ming us with anatomy, physiology, biochemistry, therapeutics and pathology, topped off with a whirlwind tour through general medicine, general surgery and the specialities, we would come out as competent doctors. The mantra 'assessment drives learn-ing' underpinned the system, and there were frequent exams to test recall of facts. Cram, test, forget; cram, test, forget. In this pre-internet era, personal knowledge was highly valued; it was hard to look things up and check the facts. Furthermore, this was also before evidence-based medicine; much of the medicine we were taught was anecdote handed down from doctor to student. There was minimal teaching about the psychological aspects of illness, and no expert patients empowered and valued for teaching us about the patient experience of health and healthcare.

The doctors who served as our role models were predominantly middle-class white males, many with attitudes and behaviours that would not be tolerated today. I had a particularly humiliating experience as a final year medical student when asked to present a case I had not prepared adequately. I was with my firm (the small group of medical students who were with me throughout my medical training) and was reduced to a jibbering wreck by the acerbic, goading and relentless questioning of a neurology registrar. I learnt how important it is to be well prepared; I also learnt how important it is for teaching and learning to be a safe experience, where the student is supported, not bullied and humiliated. This experience left me with a deep-seated fear of making a fool of myself in public.

The dean of the medical school and our senior leaders must have been aware of the shortcomings of the training, despite the imperative for doctors to 'do no harm'. But it had always been like this, we were told. There were no misgivings about unleashing yet another generation of unworldly and bookish junior doctors onto the most vulnerable and needy patients. There was little concern about *how* we as new doctors would cope emotionally, being ill-equipped to deal with the challenges ahead. The prevailing attitude in the medical profession was to resort to gallows humour; avoid being admitted to hospital in August of each year (the intake of newly qualified doctors starts in early August), and avoid ending up in the hands of clueless junior doctors. As students, we bought into the idea that medical student training in the UK was the best in the world. Our teachers and doctors created this myth, and none of us knew enough to challenge it. Furthermore, we knew that the London teaching hospitals with their long traditions were regarded as the very pinnacle of this elite system. We were proud to be part of it, blinded from seeing things as they really were. But before long, wholesale changes in British society would shake up medicine, including the training of doctors.

Medicine in the eighties was disease-focused, with little thought for social context or the impact of disease on a patient's quality of life. Our clinical practice in West London brought us into contact with a broad cross-section of society. We did not learn much about social determinants of health by studying our patients. Race was not discussed or factored in. *The Black and White Minstrel Show* was still showing on TV with its blacked-up actors. In April 1981 the first Brixton riot erupted, just two miles from my student flat in Clapham South. It lasted for three days and involved 5,000 people. Over 100 vehicles were burned, more than half of them police vehicles. A few months earlier in New Cross, thirteen black youths aged between fourteen and twenty-two had died, which went on to inspire the 'Black People's Day of Action'. The *Sun*, under the ownership of Rupert Murdoch, who went on to buy *The Times* and *The*

Sunday Times in 1981, reported the protests under the headline 'The Day the Blacks Ran Riot in London'. This was the era of heavy-handed policing and the 'sus law', used to stop and search people thanks to permissive use of the 1824 Vagrancy Act. The subsequent report, led by Lord Scarman, a former high court judge, into the 1981 Brixton Riots advised 'urgent action' to prevent racial disadvantage becoming an 'endemic, ineradicable disease threatening the very survival of our society'.

It is clear in hindsight that, like most young white men of my generation, I had a lot to learn. The two sheets of A4 paper with photos of the Charing Cross Hospital Medical School class of 1983 show a group of young, slightly anxious-looking faces. There was not a single black UK-born medical student in our year. The only two black students were both international students from Nigeria.

The early 1980s in the UK was also extremely difficult for the gay community. The AIDS pandemic was starting, and social attitudes to gay people were still mainly negative and repressed. In 1988 the Thatcher government introduced legislation that prevented the 'promotion' of homosexuality. I remember one of my friends wearing a full set of PPE just to take a history from and examine an openly gay patient; there was paranoia and hysteria about HIV, even in a medical school hospital. Imagine the impact this must have had on the patient to be treated in this way, rather than to be cared for with respect, kindness and compassion. In our year at medical school there was no student who was openly gay. However, after qualifying as a doctor, Andy gradually came out. More than twenty years later, we were to share an office in Cardiff when working in medical education.

I asked Andy what it had been like for him, being gay, yet not admitting it openly.

'It was a difficult time for me,' he told me. 'It was not just the fellow students. It was also my friends and family. When I did come out to my brother and sister they were loving and supporting. It took me a long time to come out to my parents and I wasn't fully out until I had done that. I needn't have worried about their reaction. I knew from an early age that I would always be gay. Of course, some of my friends guessed that I might be gay, particularly my female friends.'

When we weren't in lectures, the library, or the pub we spent hours watching snooker on TV. Snooker became a national obsession. It was cheap TV and, in retrospect, oddly gripping. The snooker players were celebrities, more famous than football players. It was especially popular with male medical students, providing something to do when we should have been studying and revising for the next examination. The very last game I watched was the final of the World Snooker Championship, live from the Crucible Theatre in Sheffield. It was a Sunday evening in 1980 and the game was reaching its climax. The snooker was interrupted by a live news report from the Iranian Embassy siege in South Kensington. The TV cut away from the men playing with their coloured balls, to SAS soldiers abseiling from the roof of a building and forcing entry through the first-floor windows. The SAS rescued all but one of the hostages, and killed five of the six hostage-takers. Seventeen minutes of compelling action live on prime-time national TV; it was better than James Bond. It also made me realise just how dull snooker was; I never watched it again.

Then we had a brief war. Mrs Thatcher decided to take the UK into war with Argentina in 1982 in a spat over sovereignty of the Falkland Islands. A cursory glance at a map makes it hard to sustain the fiction that these remote and barren islands are UK sovereign territory. This felt at the time like another whopper from the UK government, to be placed in the future alongside the legitimate ownership of the Elgin Marbles and the Benin Bronzes and the fantasy of Saddam Hussain's weapons of mass destruction. The national jingoism, arrogance and hubris which were prominent throughout this ten-week war unexpectedly intruded into my sense of self. For the first time in my life, I was uncomfortable with being British.

But I passed my final examinations, and was ready to be a doctor. My first junior doctor jobs would be in Plymouth, scene of some triumphant naval homecoming from the South Atlantic a few months earlier.

What could possibly go wrong?

CHAPTER 5

STARTING OUT
1983–1986

D erriford Hospital on the outskirts of Plymouth resembled a recently built tower block. Or rather, an *almost* built tower block. The money had run out and most of the hospital had been mothballed. Just a few wards were up and running; I was at the vanguard in this so-called modern hospital, which resembled a soon-to-be abandoned hospital in a field full of cows as it waited for funds, staff and patients.

Plymouth in the 1980s was going through enormous change. There was Plymouth the boom-town, with its start-up businesses and entrepreneurs attracted to new business parks on the edge of town; then there was the poor, run-down Plymouth, populated by working-class locals left behind by Thatcherism and a familiar lack of investment. The city had been heavily bombed in the Second World War by the Luftwaffe, and rebuilt in the following decades. Much of the immediate post-war social housing still survived; flimsy prefabs not much bigger than static caravans housing many of Plymouth's poor and elderly. In contrast, there were also smart housing estates popping up on greenfield sites at the edge of town. This was classic urban sprawl, with not much apparent thought about how this new housing would knit together to create sustainable and coherent communities. Plymouth was also a naval town; Her Majesty's Naval Base Devonport was one of just three such bases in the UK, the largest naval base in Western Europe, dedicated to repair of nuclear submarines and refuelling of all Royal Navy ships.

As a junior doctor working long hours, I had little time to orientate myself, although I did get to know a night club called the Sailing Club, also known as the Groin Exchange or 'GX' amongst the junior doctors; this was bravado rather than reality. It was all we could do to stay awake and dance to 'Relax' (Frankie Goes to Hollywood) or '1999' (Prince), never mind contemplate exchanging groins. I also remember lots of pubs, parks and green spaces. It was a great place and I loved being there despite its lack of charm.

I enjoyed Plymouth thanks to its residents, who relied on the seasonal work of tourism and the secure work of the naval base, but also enjoyed the calmness and laidback lifestyle of the off-season winter months. Plymouth had a friendly, welcoming feel to it, a perfect non-threatening place for me to start out as a young doctor. However, the city also had a reputation amongst medics for being the graveyard of career ambition. The lifestyle here was just too nice; they came and never left. I was also charmed by the local singsong accent; I still remember being called 'my lover' by the cashier in the canteen when I paid for my first meal at Derriford Hospital, having driven by motorbike from London to Plymouth. I would be starting work as a junior doctor the following day.

My first night on call wasn't without incident. I was asked by the nurses to catheterise an elderly man with retention of urine (he couldn't pee and was in agony). I had never catheterised a patient and had no idea how to do it. It was the middle of the night; I phoned the Senior House Officer (the person next in line) and asked what to do. He stayed in bed and talked me through the procedure on the phone. I squirted in the lubricant gel, inserted the catheter and the bag filled with urine, but then stopped; what now? More phone calls, more angst, no one willing to show me how to do this simple task. Of course, the urine stopped flowing as the bladder was now empty and the patient was no longer distressed. However, the nurses were deferential towards me and were not confident enough to reassure me that I had completed the task and could now go back to bed.

I was a doctor, but a doctor lacking useful skills. It was deflating and demoralising to be so incompetent. I felt sorry for the patients having me as their doctor. My first year was packed with such incidents; learning the hard way, making mistakes, the patients mainly uncomplaining, enduring my efforts with stoicism and bravery. Fear of hurting patients exacerbated my lack of skills; by necessity, this fear was soon replaced by a more detached approach which was more successful. Chronic sleep deprivation was the worst aspect of the work. In 1983 there was no shift pattern (twenty years later this all changed following imposition of the European Working Time Directive), or day off to recover after being up all night on call. I was working on the wards from 8 a.m. to 6 p.m. Monday to Friday. I was also regularly on call at night, and working on weekends. Being on call for the weekend meant starting work on Friday morning at 8 a.m. and finishing work the following Monday at 6 p.m. It was horrendous.

As new doctors we supported each other, and quickly acquired skills and survival techniques. We shared our disasters and soon developed a dark sense of humour as a coping strategy. Deep down we knew it was no laughing matter. 'How is it going?' friends and family would ask. 'It's fine! I am really enjoying it!' The reality was quite different, and the dropout rate for new doctors was high.

We learn from our mistakes. My worst experience in that first year would prove to be a clerical error: writing take-home prescriptions when I was tired for two elderly, terminally ill patients with lung cancer and getting the names mixed up. The ward nurses and pharmacy failed to spot my mistake (it would never happen today) and the two patients went home on each other's drugs, neither of them challenging the sudden change in their medication. Both died soon after discharge, although probably not from the prescribing error. My consultant called me in and explained what had happened; I was appalled. There was no team meeting, no team learning and no shared responsibility or acknowledgement of a systems failure. I was left alone with the burden of guilt for the error I had made. Both patients had died. The lesson learnt was to check and check again. I became obsessive about checking to avoid a repeat of this error.

From Plymouth I moved to Middlesbrough, driving the 370 miles in my Ford Escort, having sold my beloved motorbike. The hospitals in Middlesbrough were a mixed bag, from cheap, prefabricated legacy buildings from the Second World War through to Victorian redbrick, patched and made good for over 100 years. The newest was the South Cleveland Hospital, a large new building with a metal roof (as with Derriford Hospital, the money had run out and this was the cheapest option). The consultants, trainee doctors and nurses were inspiring. The work was hard, but there was lots of experience, and excellent teaching. It was August 1984; the sun shone and the air was fresh and clear, but I was completely unprepared for the sulphurous smog that settled on the town a few weeks later at the onset of colder weather. It caught the back of your throat and made you cough, eyes watering.

'You'll get used to it,' said the locals, who accepted this level of pollution as liveable, breathable, a fact of life.

Local weather conditions were responsible for trapping polluting fumes over the town, creating a toxic blanket. ICI Billingham, on the north-western fringes of Middlesbrough, was the local chemical plant and a big employer. At the time, the plant had three production units making ammonia and methanol, and one making nitric acid and methyl methacrylate (a Perspex precursor). In 1984, this plant was the largest producer of ammonia and methanol in the world. The worst air pollution in the UK was apparently a price worth paying in exchange for jobs.

I passed my physician exams quickly, but couldn't decide what career path to take. I tried haematology in Cambridge, surrounded by the Fenlands, which I explored by bike. The main attraction of Cambridge was obviously the university, which was inaccessible to the local population, including me. I wondered how the citizens of Cambridge would react if ICI Billingham was moved here to provide jobs for the local population. I could not see the dons tolerating the sulphurous smog as it settled on Cambridge for a few days.

Haematology at Addenbrooke's Hospital was academic and included complex and clever applied science. But I felt unable to cope with the emotional challenge of caring for patients with leukaemia, many of whom were young and subsequently died. We were not candid with the patients, offering false hope (it seemed to me) as the truth was too grim to admit. The logic was that hope was needed or none of the patients would submit to the rigours of chemotherapy. This made sense at the time, but it felt wrong to me. These days discussions around outcomes, what sort of future a patient is facing, are much better informed; there isn't the same old-fashioned stiff upper lip attitude that can lead to false promises.

I knew clinical haematology was not for me, but I have the professor and head of department, Robin Carroll, to thank for introducing me to medical research. It was through Carroll's support and encouragement that I secured my first academic publication, as co-author on a case report along with one of the best known doctors in the UK, Sir David Weatherall. He also inspired me by talking about science in a way that was easy to understand, and exciting. His three-dimensional computer images derived from structural protein analysis were not just pretty pictures: they provided important insights into how these proteins worked in human biology; at the time, this was a revelation. Carroll looked bemused when I announced my intention to leave haematology for primary care. He made it clear to me that he thought that I was making a mistake. Perhaps he was right?

• • •

FEMALE, LATE THIRTIES, MUSCLE AND SKIN DISEASE

In her late thirties, she has still not fully ruled out having a third child. This diagnosis changes things. Three of us are present at that consultation, the third person being the local rheumatologist. We explain that dermatomyositis is a rare condition of unknown aetiology, characterised by the immune system attacking the skin and muscles, creating inflammation. Fortunately, her muscles are minimally affected. Even her skin disease is milder than usual for this condition. She seems relieved, but is still uncertain what treatment to go for.

'The blood tests have revealed a rare antibody, Jo-1, seen in just 10 per cent of patients with dermatomyositis, and often associated with scaly thickened skin on the hands and feet, as in your case,' I explain.

We discuss treatment options, giving time for her to take it all in and to process the information. I write down the names of the drugs, and give her two websites for further reading. No decision on treatment is made today.

'And the question of having another baby?' she asks, falteringly.

'Probably best to wait for now, to see how things go over the next few months,' replies my colleague.

CHAPTER 6

A TASTE OF GENERAL PRACTICE

1987–1988

After haematology, I went into general practice in York, appointed to a job rotation on a sought-after GP training scheme. I was fortunate to have an inspiring GP trainer who taught me a different style of doctoring. General practice was a welcome change after hospital medicine. The front-line in UK medicine, general practice requires a wide range of knowledge and skills. The philosophy underpinning general practice at the time was holistic medicine, the concept of the patient as the central focus, and the doctor tasked with considering the 'whole patient'. The teaching we received as GP trainees was like returning to medical school and acquiring the essential skills and attitudes that had been omitted from our training. We started from basics, with social awareness, reflection and self-awareness. As GP trainees we were learning basic doctoring skills for the first time, including how to deal with our own hubris, ego and self-interest.

My GP trainer, Dr Gerry Jackson, was a gifted teacher and role model. We met once a week at his home to discuss the psycho-social aspects of medicine and healthcare. It was a style of doctoring which I soon recognised as being important for more effective doctor–patient relations, one I have retained throughout my subsequent career. Many of our sessions concerned the need for me to focus more on the person in front of me rather than on the abstract human body:

'What did you make of Mrs Davies who you saw on Monday afternoon, with tummy ache?'

'Diverticulitis?' I tried. 'Or maybe irritable bowel syndrome? Or perhaps a peptic ulcer or gastritis? I prescribed antacids for symptomatic relief, and was going to see her again next week to see how she is getting on.'

'…and her alcohol consumption?' said Gerry.

'I forgot to ask her. I will make a point of asking next week.'

'*Oh, it's not too much, doctor…*' Gerry adopted a falsetto voice.

'Let's be a little bit more precise than that, Mrs Davies. How much, exactly, are you drinking each day?' I said.

'Oh, I'm not too sure. Perhaps a couple of whiskeys before bed.'

'Is that small whiskeys or large ones?'

'Bottles,' says Gerry.

'Really?'

'Yes, really!'

'I would have never guessed. She seems so…'

'Respectable? Well turned out?'

Yes, all of these things. I felt foolish.

'The next time you see her,' said Gerry, 'get close enough to see how she smells.'

A few days later, during my evening clinic, I leant forward and sniffed a combination of perfume and spearmint. I reported back to Gerry, proud to have completed this mission so successfully.

'And your conclusion is...?'

'Nothing from her smell to suggest that she is drinking excessively.'

A glint in his eye suggested this was what Gerry was expecting me to say. I had walked straight into his trap.

'Female alcoholics often use perfume and mints to conceal the smell of booze on their breath. Whenever I smell strong perfume in my female patients, I ask myself what they are trying to hide. Alcoholics are often adept at keeping up appearances, particularly the women. In contrast to the stereotypical alcoholics you learn about at medical school, their lives do not necessarily disintegrate. Mrs Davies has been drinking one to two bottles of whiskey per day for a number of years. She is a regular at the bottle bank, but always uses the one at Sainsbury's. You know the one? It's at the far end of the car park and not used very much. Less chance of being spotted by someone she knows.'

It was all so obvious when Gerry explained it to me like this. I needed to put my Freudian hat on and study human behaviour. Despite having passed my exams, I still had a lot to learn.

* * *

General practice was regarded as a soft option by hospital doctors, whilst, at the same time, GPs were quietly envied for their lifestyle choice. Hospital doctors consoled themselves by regarding general practice as a second-rate career, lacking the glamour and prestige of being a specialist in the hospital. If anything, this view has become more entrenched over the last thirty years, as the gap between hospital medicine and general practice has widened. GPs and hospital doctors now rarely meet up; we are not on first name terms; we rarely attend the same educational meetings; we tend not to speak on the phone. It's all at arm's length, with almost no face-to-face interaction or interface for discourse and human engagement. It is hard to reconcile this with my positive experiences as a GP trainee in York in the late 1980s, where GPs were held in high esteem, as valued members of the local healthcare team. Importantly, the hospital doctors and the GPs in York met up once weekly at the hospital 'grand round', a clinical meeting where cases of interest were presented for learning and discussion. The GPs and hospital doctors in York were on first-name terms, the medical community was cohesive and well-integrated; the beneficiaries were the patients. This insight would be central to my plans more than thirty years later to create a new way of working for dermatology in my patch of North Wales, based on the best part of the old way of working.

One of the things Gerry emphasised was the flexibility of a career in general practice.

'You can create a job to suit yourself,' he told me. 'For the first twenty years of being a GP I did a day per week as an anaesthetist at the local hospital. I enjoyed being part of the hospital team, and hearing what was going on. It gave me insight into the mentality of hospital doctors. I also started to understand *medical politics*.'

This was Gerry's other gift to me.

*   *   *

On the night of the 1987 hurricane, the BBC weatherman Michael Fish got it wrong.

'A woman rang the BBC and said that she heard there was a hurricane on the way; well, if you're watching, don't worry, there isn't.'

Poor Michael Fish. He was much loved by the British public; the longest serving broadcast meteorologist on television, he never quite recovered from this blunder, and nor did the Met Office.

That night I was on-call for obstetrics at Hillingdon Hospital, a very busy obstetrics unit, serving the multi-ethnic population of West London. It was an era when the midwives were not permitted to do much; nearly everything was done by the doctors, and much of this fell to the most junior doctor on call. That was me. Having been awake, working hard, for eighteen hours, I was not at my most alert during the hurricane. The walk between the doctors' on-call room and the labour ward was about 150 metres. I must have done this walk at least ten times that night, but failed to spot that it was windier than usual. In contrast to most of the UK population, who slept through the hurricane, I was very much awake and exposed to it; but it completely failed to register. Sleep deprivation does that. Never mind the weather, what about the labouring women and their babies? I can't remember much about them either, but still have a sneaking suspicion that someone else might have done a better job sewing up their episiotomies and vaginal splits and tears. It is hard to describe what the vulva looks like following childbirth. It's tricky to know which bit goes where when the tissues are swollen and bruised and there's rapid bleeding from the traumatised vagina, in addition to a steady loss of blood from the inside of the uterus. All of this calls for a highly skilled and experienced obstetrician, fresh and alert; instead, they had to make do with me. I hope that my wonky vulval sewing did not have too profoundly negative effects on the subsequent love lives of these uncomplaining women.

I finally managed to grab some sleep, but was up again at 7:30 a.m., shaving whilst listening to the radio. I heard the news about the hurricane: 135 mph winds, 15 million trees felled and eighteen people killed. Many of my colleagues were unable to make it to work that day, as roads and transport were so disrupted. I was stranded on the front line, exhausted, with no sign of relief. Intuitively, I knew that this style of medicine was not for me.

●　　●　　●

June 1987 saw Margaret Thatcher's Conservative party win a third consecutive victory; a landslide majority of 102 seats, ushering in another four years of chipping away at public services and slowly starving the NHS. In contrast to Labour, whose leader Neil Kinnock focused on the high rate of unemployment and long NHS waiting lists, the Conservatives focused on lower taxes, a strong economy and defence. It seems quaint in hindsight that the political debate in this election campaign included the somewhat hypothetical question of what each party would do to prevent Russia invading the UK (Perestroika was only two years in the making). The NHS was already in decline, but this fact had failed to make it to the top of the political agenda. Rather than focus on improving the NHS, the Conservatives were obsessed with strong defence and riven by uncertainty about Europe. Thatcher's hostility to the European community was an issue which contributed to her downfall, and was to plague her successor, John Major. No one seemed to notice that being invaded by Russia was unlikely, but underinvestment in the NHS was now a chronic problem of far higher importance. On a positive note for multi-racial Britain, however, three black MPs were elected into parliament: Diane Abbott, Paul Boateng and Bernie Grant. There was a growing sense that things were starting to change in the UK, and the old assumptions about society no longer applied.

●　　●　　●

BLACK AFRICAN MALE, AGED FORTY-FIVE, PSORIASIS

Jide is from Mali. Since arriving in the UK in 2018, he has developed psoriasis. It is extensive; he is shedding skin; it is affecting his self-confidence. 'Your skin smells different,' his wife told him; their love life has wilted. Jide is working as a carer in a community psychiatric facility. He attends my clinic, frustrated by the lack of progress with treating his psoriasis. We go through the options again. 'How about phototherapy?' I suggest. He is sceptical, having not had this treatment before. 'Let's go and see the phototherapy unit so you can discuss this treatment in more detail.' I leave him with the nurses, and come back twenty minutes later having seen another patient in the interim. He smiles at me. 'I'll give it a go. They have explained it very well. We can try and hope.'

A few weeks later I asked our lead nurse for phototherapy how Jide is doing. 'He's nearly clear. Such a nice man. Did you know he comes from Timbuktu?'

CHAPTER 7

DR JULIAN TUDOR HART, MEDICAL HERO

1986-1988

A key part of training to be a GP was learning to fill in a trainee log book. We were expected to write about our experiences as a trainee GP, and to reflect on how we had done, and what we might do differently next time. It was like keeping a personal diary, but one that others might also read from time to time, focused on professional issues and day to day patient care. This reflective diary was ahead of its time, anticipating contemporary 'reflective practice' by about thirty years. It is now at the core of all medical training, and is also a key element in doctor's appraisal and revalidation systems.

Three months after joining Gerry and his partners at the Upper Poppleton GP surgery in York, I recorded my day as follows:

Dr Jackson (Gerry) always measures and records patient's blood pressure, whatever they present with. I have never seen any doctor who is more conscientious about this. When I asked Gerry about this, he informed me it had not always been this way. He told me it all changed with Dr Julian Tudor Hart.

A week later:

Great tutorial today. Gerry told me about Dr Julian Tudor Hart. For years GPs had felt like the poor relations of the hospital consultants. Then Tudor Hart came along. One man changed the landscape! No wonder Gerry was so excited. JTH had his practice in Glyncorrwg, a mining community in South Wales, not far from the M4 and steelworks at Port Talbot. His blood pressure monitoring study was published in the Lancet *in 1970.*

JTH set about screening the whole *primary care population in his practice for raised blood pressure. He managed to get data on blood pressure for 98 per cent of his patients. Glyncorrwg is in West Glamorgan, an isolated, industrial village population. Most of the men were coal miners in the local mine or steel workers down the road in Port Talbot. Gerry particularly excited that JTH managed to do this without increasing the rate of home visits or consultations in the health centre. In other words, JTH did this as part of his everyday routine practice; blood pressure recording in everyone was part of the normal day.*

Some of the patients with raised blood pressure already had early signs of kidney and heart damage, as the raised blood pressure had been undiagnosed. By starting anti-hypertensive therapy earlier, JTH was preventing further damage from occurring. Now understand why Gerry always measures BP.

Our teachers at Charing Cross Hospital Medical School had forgotten to tell us about this important piece of research from primary care published just a few years earlier. It was research done in everyday clinical practice, on a common disease, in an NHS practice, and had come up with important findings. It was pragmatic and important, and would be the benchmark for my own style of research in future years. For Gerry, this research was both validation for primary care and also helped to underpin his own identity as a GP at the top of his game.

JTH was also a communist.

I didn't know any communists. I was fascinated. Did Gerry mean a communist like Lenin, Stalin and Mao, or was he referring to British communists like the characters in Doris Lessing's *The Golden Notebook*, who saw themselves as fashionable radicals?

Gerry was an *Independent*-reading Liberal Democrat.

I could see that this discovery would have surprised him.

'Did Tudor Hart do anything else?' I asked.

'Yes.' Gerry's face lit up. 'The year after publishing the blood pressure study in the *Lancet*, he published a population-based study on provision of healthcare and its relationship to poverty and wealth. He related this to the principles of the NHS: free healthcare for all at the point of delivery. Tudor Hart argued the case brilliantly and came up with the concept of "the inverse care law".'

Why hadn't they taught us about *this* at medical school?

Gerry handed me a photocopy of another *Lancet* paper, reading aloud from the final paragraph:

> 'In areas with the most sickness and death, general practitioners have more work, larger lists, less hospital support, and inherit more clinically ineffective traditions of consultation, than in the healthiest areas; and hospital doctors shoulder heavier case-loads with less staff and equipment, more obsolete buildings, and suffer recurrent crises in the availability of beds and replacement staff. These trends can be summed up as the inverse care law: that the availability of good medical care tends to vary inversely with the need of the population served.'

Gerry was clearly excited by this. We went through the paper in more detail, discussing each paragraph, trying to better understand the evidence which had been cited. I too was excited, feeling that the inverse care law would turn out to be a fundamental concept for assessing health services as a means of delivering on social justice and equality. This was the first time in my career that I had started to grapple with the political dimensions of health care. How appropriate that this should have been via the passionate teaching of my guide and mentor, the Liberal Democrat-voting Dr Gerry Jackson.

Although residents of Upper Poppleton, the location of Gerry's health centre, were clearly well-served by the inverse care law, his practice also covered Acomb, a relatively deprived suburb of York with lots of patients living close to or in poverty. Despite this, healthcare in York was far removed from health care in Glyncorrwg. I would soon learn more about inequality in health care services by working in South Wales, an area that included multiple, poor Welsh mining communities including Glyncorrwg.

* * *

I was not yet ready to commit to a career in general practice. Gerry wasn't offended by this news. Although I had personally benefited from his sessions, and had acquired a far better under-standing about what it was to be a doctor, I had found myself dreading the on-calls. In the pre-mobile phone era, GPs did their own on-call using their home phone and a pager for emergencies, getting up in the middle of the night to drive to an unfamiliar house and meet people they didn't know, to assess a sick baby or an elderly person, to witness 'domestics' too, with drunk and aggressive patients feeling unwell in their own homes.

On-call was done in addition to the Monday to Friday day time work as a GP. I decided to invite my girlfriend Sarah (later to be my wife) for a weekend on-call, to see how she would cope with answering the phone, taking messages, and spending time supporting me as I was working. GP wives were paid a small fee for these duties in that era. Sarah coped well, but I didn't. It felt odd having my girlfriend involved in my work; Sarah had her own career as a food writer and cookery editor for women's magazines. She should have been free to pursue that, without having to take on GP-support duties. I decided to try hospital medicine again, refreshed and fired up following my sojourn in general practice.

My experience of working as a GP in primary care revealed two medical specialities which generated a lot of work but were poorly served by the local specialists: dermatology and rheumatology. Despite training at medical school being all too brief for these two disciplines, it had also been inspiring. The small amount of teaching we received revealed that both specialities were interesting, important and research-active. At the forefront of this research was Professor 'Tiny' Maini, a rheumatologist based at the Kennedy Institute of Rheumatology, and part of Charing Cross Hospital Medical School. Professor Maini's talks had a profound effect on me. Lecturing without notes, speaking clearly as he developed his ideas, he drew students into his world of inflammatory arthritis; it was a revelation. In subsequent years his research was to have an impact on both rheumatology and dermatology across the globe, with the development of so-called biological therapies to treat chronic inflammatory diseases. Few of our lecturers had the ability to link research with clinical medicine in this way. Prof Maini made rheumatology feel exciting and relevant.

In my short attachment to dermatology as a medical student, I'd also been lucky enough to study under Dr Geoff Cream, another gifted clinical teacher, who opened up dermatology as a discipline of great importance and interest. You could actually see the skin diseases, providing a totally different world of patient and doctor experience compared to diseases and conditions affecting other human organs. Furthermore, Dr Cream explained how dermatology and rheumatology overlapped, both in the diseases seen by the two specialities, and the treatments that were used. This was an important example of joined-up medicine: two specialities, but often one disease process taking place in the same patient.

I applied for a job in dermatology in High Wycombe. The two consultants I would be working for both had strong reputations as researchers. This would be my first exposure to medical research since my first tentative attempts at Addenbrooke's Hospital in haematology. Furthermore, one of the consultants wanted me to do some preparatory reading of key research papers before I started. I was excited by the prospect of working in dermatology, but also nervous about what the consultant meant by 'hitting the ground running'. I had visions of falling flat on my face.

* * *

TEENAGE BOY WITH HIVES

Stephen is seventeen and has been booked as an extra at the end of my evening GP surgery. Mum insisted on an urgent appointment, saying he was covered in an itchy rash and that his lips had swelled to a huge size.

'Have you had this before?' I ask.

'Yes, I get hives, but never this bad, and not usually with swelling of the lips.'

'What were you doing before this attack came on?' I ask.

'Not much,' he replies. 'I sprained my ankle yesterday playing football and have been dosing myself up with ibuprofen.'

I check him over, and examine his skin. It was an impressive rash, and his lips are still swollen.

'I think it's the ibuprofen,' I announce. *'It lowers the threshold for urticaria, and can sometimes cause severe attacks like this one. Just avoid taking any more and take one of these antihistamines twice daily.'*

I hand him a prescription.

'So it's not anaphylaxis?' he asks.

'No, it's not. We call this urticaria with angioedema.'

'Mum will be relieved. I think she thought that I was dying.'

CHAPTER 8

PUBLISH OR PERISH

1988–1992

The 260-bed general hospital in High Wycombe was not an obvious place to find an academic dermatology unit. I had joined a department with two bosses who, obsessed with research, academic publishing and academic writing, churned out papers and inspired the rest of the team to do the same. It was the medical equivalent of having landed in a high-performing university department. Weekends were spent in the dermatology library at Wycombe General Hospital, overlooking the football ground of Wycombe Wanderers Football Club, writing research papers. On one Saturday in April 1989, with the radio football commentary on in the background, the FA Cup semi-final between Liverpool and Nottingham Forest, I was shocked to hear the disaster from Hillsborough unfolding. Ninety-six fans died, 766 were injured. This was even more shocking following so soon after the Bradford City stadium fire in 1985, which had caused fifty-six deaths and 265 injuries. The Popplewell Inquiry for the Bradford City fire had made recommendations to improve ground safety which were clearly not far-reaching enough. These tragic events affected me greatly, challenging the notion of the UK as a safe country, at ease with itself. This was reinforced by the experiences of the unfortunate bereaved families, with abuse from the *Sun* newspaper, and a police force quick to apportion blame but reluctant to accept responsibility. More than thirty years later, no one has been found accountable for these deaths, deemed at the second coroner's inquest as being unlawful killings caused by grossly negligent failures by police and ambulance services. This was described in 2021 by the Conservative Leader of the House of Commons as 'the greatest scandal of British policing of our lifetimes'.

It was now easier for me to turn my back on following football; career progress in dermatology required a new level of commitment. Success would be judged by clinical research, as measured by my academic publishing. I wrote case reports, case series, and review articles, low-level academic writing, which allowed me to improve my scholarly skills.

My first case report concerned multiple self-healing melanomas in a patient with the rare disorder xeroderma pigmentosum, a condition characterised by an inability for the body to repair DNA damage. It is usually lethal, leading to early death in the teens or twenties from skin cancer. Our patient had survived into his sixties despite having multiple malignant melanomas.

Six months later, I was invited to present this case at the dermatology section of the Royal Society of Medicine. When the audience of over 200 people roared with laughter, I felt both gratified (they weren't asleep) and concerned (it wasn't a joke). When they eventually calmed down, a female dermatologist in her early sixties stood up to speak.

'Yes, I have a question.' She was towards the back of the auditorium. The lecture theatre was hushed, everyone listening intently to what she had to say. She had a strong voice for such a small woman, with a distinctive Scottish accent. She spoke clearly, carefully enunciating every word, and projecting her voice so that everyone could hear her, including me on the stage.

'You are asking us to believe that this man with xeroderma pigmentosum had twelve well-documented examples of malignant melanoma, a number of which were ulcerated, in two instances with a polypoid tumour, and yet survived and is still alive today, nearly forty years later?'

The mood in the lecture theatre changed from reverence to pity.

'Yes,' I croaked, my mouth dry, my palms sweaty.

A low gasp from the auditorium. This was shaping up to be a car crash, with me as the victim.

Then a little voice (mine) started speaking, and the audience had no choice but to listen. I too was listening, interested to hear what I had to say, seemingly a casual observer:

'The thing is,' I said, 'we managed to retrieve ten of the twelve specimen blocks; the two oldest had been destroyed. All of the retrieved samples have now been reviewed by an experienced pathologist. The latest tumour markers, not available when most of these biopsies were taken, have been used too. The results were unambiguous: all ten showed malignant melanomas, mostly falling into the thicker poor prognosis groups.'

'Doesn't this all seem to be a little far-fetched and counter-intuitive to you?' she said.

'Counterintuitive? Yes, of course,' I conceded. 'Which explains why we are presenting the case today. Far-fetched? No, we don't think so. It is our belief that the facts of the case as presented today speak for themselves. There has been no exaggeration or omission. That's the point we want to make. It is not possible to reconcile what has happened to our patient with our knowledge of the natural history and behaviour of malignant melanoma. Something extraordinary is going on in this patient, which we are now in the process of studying. We are collaborating with skin tumour biology experts at St Thomas's Hospital who hope to shed light on how our patient's immune system has gained the upper hand and has been able to keep these multiple melanomas at bay.'

She sat down, apparently satisfied with my answer. There was a buzz in the lecture theatre at the outcome of our verbal tussle. It seemed I had done OK.

'What was that all about?' I asked my boss after the meeting.

'Don't worry. That was only Professor Rona Mackie from Glasgow,' he said.

Professor Mackie was, I discovered, the UK's top melanoma expert, with a fearsome reputation. The reason for the laughter was that I had presented the case as if it were perfectly normal to develop twelve bad-prognosis melanomas and still survive for nearly four decades. It was the laughter of incredulity. At the end of the meeting Professor Mackie agreed to look at the skin histology samples from this patient. We sent the slides to her in Glasgow; a few weeks later she confirmed the diagnosis and our interpretation. We acknowledged Professor Mackie in the paper which was accepted for publication in the *British Journal of Dermatology*, one of my first publications.

I soon had four or five papers on the go at any one time, and was publishing at a steady rate. This was the ideal environment to learn how to write articles and to get them published. Both of my bosses thought nothing about starting the day early and finishing late in their determination to do research as well as NHS work. The younger of the two was at the peak of her powers, always telling patients what 'we' thought was going on and what 'we' recommended should be done next, and what 'we' believed was the explanation. It was kind of her to use 'we' when with me, as I was clueless at this stage of my training, and she rarely sought my opinion. The patients trusted her.

My other boss was more conventional; John was a big character who was warm in his personal interactions and generous with his time. He exhibited hyperactivity and boundless enthusiasm which the rest of us tried to keep up with. He was positive about everything, and was loved by us all, including the patients. He seemed to have confidence in me, and encouraged me to get going with academic writing and presentations. Whenever I now bump into John at meetings, we always make time for a catch-up and laugh together.

Looking back, few of the papers I published made any impact on improving patient care. I was unaware that this was the prime aim of medical research. Nevertheless, I was learning my craft: how to carry out clinical research and to write papers, skills that would become central to my career as a dermatologist. Importantly, the department gave me security and support. It was a nurturing environment for a dermatologist, one in which I was encouraged to develop and grow; occasional failures were tolerated. My two bosses became role models; they personified the type of dermatologist I wanted to be – curious, compassionate, well-informed and free from hubris. Fenella was appointed as an honorary professor of dermatology in Oxford. John was appointed as the medical director in his NHS trust, the top doctor in the organisation. If a sprinkle of their stardust brushed off on me, I might be OK.

●　　●　　●

I began plotting my next move, but trying to get a job as a dermatology registrar in London proved more difficult than anticipated. I generally made the shortlist, but there always seemed to be an internal candidate, someone waiting in the wings, doing a research job or similar.

'Can you name the dermatology pathology textbook you're currently using?' I was asked.

As it happened, I couldn't, as I was not using one.

At the next interview the lead consultant, a legend in the world of dermatology, whom I admired for his high quality research into psoriasis and the rare blistering disease dermatitis herpetiformis, picked dirt from under his fingernails and asked a series of incurious questions. I realised I was there to make up the numbers.

Next interview.

Here I was asked: 'Was your training in general practice a bolthole for when you failed in dermatology?'

I cracked a smile.

He then asked me to spell 'pruritus', the medical term for itch; I had written *puritus* in a sentence on my curriculum vitae.

Oh well.

Landing a job at St Thomas's Hospital was clearly a stretch. I was so sure of not being chosen that I was relaxed, and answered the questions with confidence. We were expected to wait outside the interview room afterwards, to accept or decline the job if offered at the end of the interviews. I left early, saying goodbye to my fellow interviewees, and asking them to accept the job on my behalf that, once again, I wasn't offered.

Meanwhile, I was steadily adding more publications to my curriculum vitae, and presenting more cases at the monthly meeting of the dermatology section of the Royal Society of Medicine. Eventually I was interviewed for a registrar job at St Bartholomew's Hospital in London, and was appointed. By this time my CV was pretty good, both of my bosses supported me strongly, and there was no internal candidate. However, this was the only post where I was warned by my referees of the need to be wary of one of the two consultants, who had a reputation as a bully.

As things turned out, this was prescient advice.

*   *   *

At Barts the research clinic was focused on the autoimmune skin condition systemic sclerosis. This is a condition where the skin becomes hardened and scar-like, with painful loss of blood flow to the peripheries, and tightening of the skin on the hands, face and around the mouth. There were few disease-modifying treatments, and those that were available were toxic and potentially dangerous to use. The consultant in charge had collected together a group of patients with this very rare condition, giving us the opportunity to create new insights into presentation, disease progression, patient care and treatment. But we were amateurish and unprofessional in our approach, with no formal links to a university and no academics working within the research team. There is too much at stake with medical research to risk missing out on research papers due to an unfocused approach. I carried on publishing minor academic papers whilst I worked at Barts to keep my CV ticking over, but this would not be enough for promotion. I needed to use my initiative to secure access to other research teams that were more professional and productive.

My predecessor as registrar at Barts had lost hope of career progression in dermatology – it was a competitive field – and moved on to working as a GP in the West Country. It was clear to me that I needed to show ambition and far-sightedness; I needed to conduct research with a team outside my own training department. I knew that doing this was fraught with difficulty, and it might reflect badly on my two bosses (after all, they should have been creating the research opportunities within our department).

My first break came from within our own hospital. We had two patients in quick succession who came close to dying soon after starting treatment with a drug to suppress their immune systems: within four weeks of starting azathioprine, both developed sudden-onset and profound bone marrow failure. It was no one's fault, and was completely unexpected; azathioprine was not known to produce such life-threatening toxicity so soon after being started. Both of the patients were treated in the intensive care unit and eventually recovered, once azathioprine was stopped. I was encouraged to write up their cases for publication. In my efforts to understand what had happened to these patients, I met the consultant haematologist at Barts who had been involved in their care who put me in touch with someone he thought might be able to help, a PhD scientist in Sheffield.

Lynne, the scientist in question, had a hunch that she knew the answer. We sent her blood samples; she was correct. Both patients had a rare but well-documented genetic abnormality in a key enzyme which breaks down this drug and renders it inactive. It was well known in the pharmacology literature, but unknown in clinical medicine. This was pre-internet, which meant that research progress in one field of medicine could easily be overlooked by others working in a different field. I worked up the two cases, presented them at meetings and soon published the report. Although just a case report, it was one of the most significant papers I was to publish, eventually leading to the introduction of a routine test used by all clinicians in all specialities around the world who prescribe this drug. Furthermore, this single case report led to nine other publications on this topic in the following years, including first author of the clinical guidelines for azathioprine in dermatology. I had been the first clinician to recognise the clinical relevance of this research and to bring it to a wider audience. This recognition and understanding of the science's relevance to clinical medicine is now referred to as 'translational research'. At last, my research efforts were contributing to better patient care.

I was on my way.

My second break came when I was invited to help a well-known dermatologist write up a series of unusual and important cases he had gathered together. The professor concerned was old school, well-liked by everyone, based at a top research institute. Softly spoken, with a slight lisp, he was revered for his strong record of research. Understanding the need to seek permission from my bosses to release me for one afternoon each week to work on this project, he asked them on my behalf. My consultants agreed, giving me an extraordinary opportunity to work with a top figure in dermatology at a well-known research institute. The work went well. Much to his surprise, my professor came to work one day and found that I had written first drafts of both papers. He was delighted and immediately set about redrafting my initial efforts. I had taken ownership of this research through a pre-emptive strike, which ensured that I would be first author on both papers. The papers were published a few months later in high-ranking journals.

'I have become a writer,' I wrote in my diary.

Dermatology was much more academic than I had expected. The old maxim 'publish or perish' certainly held true then, as it does today. As dermatologists did no on-call, evenings and weekends are free. Where other disciplines would be on-call or recovering from being on-call, dermatologists were free to go home and reflect on their clinical activities. This gave us the opportunity to do academic work in our free time. I had never been busier (nor happier and more fulfilled). I certainly didn't miss the on-call.

* * *

ASIAN GIRL WITH WHITE PATCHES OF SKIN

Shehnaz is just twelve years old and has three white patches of skin: on the right knee, the left forearm, and the right side of the face, close to the lips. They have developed over the last six months. All three patches are small, but the affected skin looks very white in contrast to Shehnaz's dark brown skin. She was born in the UK, her parents both nurses from Kerala, India. They look worried. This is typical vitiligo, I explain, a common condition that affects about 1 per cent of the world's population. Will it get better, they want to know? Unlikely, I reply. In most cases it persists. What about treatment, they ask? My heart sinks. I recently co-authored UK treatment guidelines for vitiligo, which were published in the BMJ. I know the medical evidence well; no treatment is very effective. I explain the therapeutic ladder, which starts with immune-modulating creams and ointments. They are keen to start something immediately.

'Let's try to nip it in the bud,' suggests dad, trying to sound upbeat. I can see that both parents are devastated, aware of the stigma attached to vitiligo in India, where leprosy of the skin also produces white patches. This is sure to affect Shehnaz's future marriage prospects.

CHAPTER 9

WALES BECKONS

1991

The phone rang. It was 9:30 a.m. I had overslept. It was the dermatology secretary.

'I have Dr MacDonald on the phone,' she told me.

'Where are you?' he demanded.

'I'm at home' I replied.

'Why are you at home?' he barked.

'We've had a baby.'

'Is everything OK?'

'Yes, Sarah and the baby are fine'.

'Then get dressed and come to work immediately.'

I knew it was a research clinic that morning, normally with three doctors (one consultant, one senior registrar and me). There would be six patients at the most. I knew that I was not needed, and that they would cope without me. Nevertheless, I dressed quickly, leaving home without breakfast.

When I arrived at work, the other members of the department looked at me with worried expressions.

'He's in there,' someone whispered. I knocked on the door. 'Come in.'

He didn't invite me to sit down. How could I be so unprofessional? What was I thinking? How dare I behave like this? He would not stand for it! There would be consequences. I started crying, I couldn't stop myself. My emotions were scrambled. I began to sob loudly.

I left his office, and tried to hold myself together. The senior registrar put her arms around me. I started crying again.

'I hate that fucking bastard!' I said.

'So do I,' she said, nervously fingering her pearls.

In those days, the senior consultant's opinion was crucial for the career advancement of the trainees. It was not uncommon for consultants to phone each other before the interviews. This was the old boy network. The opposite was also possible, where the senior consultant tried to hobble the chances of a candidate who had let him down, offended him or disappointed in some way, as in my case.

I had applied for a senior registrar post in Cardiff. Dr MacDonald was one of my referees. He was sure to go out of his way to try to stop me from reaching my goal. My second referee was my first boss from High Wycombe, the one who had warned me that this man was a bully. We discussed tactics and he offered to phone the professor of dermatology in Cardiff to put in a good word. This was using the old boy network to resist the old boy network. He would make a point of explaining that he had advised me not to accept the registrar job at Barts because of the reputation of the senior consultant. In other words, he was taking responsibility for the fact that things had gone wrong, although it was certainly not his fault.

Dermatology in Cardiff was a hierarchy with a charismatic professor at its head, under whom worked a large team. There were master's degree and PhD candidates and post-doctorate researchers too. My CV was now strong for research, with a respectable number of publications, some in good journals. I explained at interview that I was now keen to do a research degree, preferably a medical doctorate; if appointed, would I be supported in this goal?

I was appointed, and yes, I would be supported with this ambition.

* * *

FEMALE, EARLY FIFTIES, RED EARS

A woman in her early fifties with bright red, very tender, slightly floppy, swollen ears. It has come on suddenly over the previous six weeks. She lives in Essex, commuting into London for a well-paid secretarial post in a stockbroker's office. I call in the consultant, but am sure I know what it is. We both agree. It is the rare immune-mediated condition which attacks cartilage, relapsing polychondritis.

'Yes, it can be treated,' I explain. 'However, it will require strong drugs to suppress your immune system, starting with oral steroids.'

'Is that safe?' she asks. 'My nan took steroid tablets for her kidney disease and ended up with a moon face.'

We discuss it in more detail. I explain that the steroid dosage should not be too high, and we will also start her on a steroid-

sparing drug. As things improve, we will then tail off the steroids and keep her on the steroid-sparing drug. She will need some time off work. She smiles, liking this suggestion.

'What about the floppy ears?' she asks. 'I feel like a spaniel.'

'Let's wait and see,' I say. 'Hopefully they will regain their normal stiffness with time.'

However, it is hard to predict; I've never seen a case of relapsing polychondritis before. The tenderness and pain in her ears should respond rapidly to treatment, and she will soon be sleeping better. But the floppy ears might stay floppy.

CHAPTER 10

ARCHIE COCHRANE, MEDICAL HERO

1968–1994

Dr Julian Tudor Hart (JTH) had come to Cardiff in the late 1960s in order to progress his career and learn about research from Archie Cochrane, the well-known and charismatic epidemiologist. Archie Cochrane was subsequently to become one of the most influential doctors in the history of medicine and is now credited as being the founding father of evidence-based medicine. He was to become another key figure and inspiration in my own professional development as a clinical academic.

JTH had been working in London as a GP, but his ambition had always been to follow in his father's footsteps as a GP to a coal mining community. He worked with Archie Cochrane on a part-time basis in order to develop his epidemiological interests. The pair had an immediate natural bond, not only on account of the strength of their shared research interests but also on account of Cochrane's contact with Tudor Hart's father during the Spanish Civil War. Cochrane recognised his potential from the start, but realised it was unlikely that Tudor Hart would stay as an epidemiologist.

As expected, Tudor Hart departed for a job as a GP following completion of just one survey. Cochrane recalled Tudor Hart's farewell as follows: 'Archie, you're OK. You are doing good, but you are not doing it very fast. I think by changing to primary care I can have a much quicker effect.'

Just like William Osler, the world famous physician of fifty years earlier, Tudor Hart was devoted to excellent patient care in tandem with being a prolific medical writer and publisher of important academic papers. Both would prove to be influential doctor role models, their insights, scholarship and lack of hubris winning admirers far beyond their immediate spheres of clinical practice.

The key to Tudor Hart's research, which brought him worldwide renown, was the remarkable and sustained cooperation of his 2,000 patients, given in return for his unswerving commitment to them. As a lifelong socialist and one-time Communist Party candidate, he was a staunch defender of the founding principles of the NHS, which marked its seventieth anniversary in the week of his death.

•   •   •

I was to learn about Archie Cochrane, Tudor Hart's mentor, whilst conducting dermatology clinics at Llandough Hospital, Penarth, the same hospital that Archie Cochrane had been based at when he did his ground-breaking research. The Medical Research Council had chosen Llandough Hospital to set up a Pneumoconiosis Research Unit in 1945 (pneumoconiosis is lung disease caused by inhaled dust in miners). Archie Cochrane was employed there from 1948 until 1960. In due course the unit was to change focus, becoming the Medical Research Council Epidemiology Unit in the early 1960s, with Cochrane as its honorary director until 1969 and then director from 1969–1974.

Cochrane was adept at spotting inconsistencies in health care and patient treatment. He was brilliant at skewering unsubstantiated medical dogma, and challenging its very existence. His life's work was to establish and promote the primacy of randomised controlled trials above any other level of evidence to measure the effectiveness of treatments.

'Too much of what was being done in the name of health care lacked scientific validation,' said Cochrane when reflecting on the NHS at the end of the 1950s. 'I had sufficient contact with the working of hospitals and clinics and the delivery of health care generally to be dismayed by what passed as service. I was troubled by the variable and curious prescribing of general practitioners, the all too varied reasons for referring patients to hospital, the attitudes and behaviour of the consultants they encountered there, and the variable ways in which death certificates were completed.'

His book *Effectiveness and Efficiency: Random Reflections on Health Services*, published in 1972, had been written in response to his dismay at the inefficiency of much of the NHS health care that he observed. His thesis was that the NHS must change to become more effective; the book explained how this should be done. It was short, at under 100 pages, but packed a big punch. To Cochrane's evident amazement, it soon became a bestseller: 'My little book *Effectiveness and Efficiency* made far more of an impact than I would ever have imagined.' The *Sunday Times* carried a full-page article on the book and it was translated into many languages. Not bad for a book he wrote in just a few

weeks, last thing each night from 10 p.m. to 1 a.m., sustained by whiskey to meet the promised deadline. 'I date the real beginnings of my love of whiskey to this period,' he would later write. It was his succinctness and clarity of purpose that made this short book so compelling.

Cochrane's advocacy of randomised controlled trials is credited as a key driver which eventually led to the development of the Cochrane Library, a virtual library database of systematic reviews, the establishment of the UK Cochrane Centre in Oxford, and the International Cochrane Collaboration (now respectively called Cochrane UK and Cochrane Collaboration). Most systematic reviews include a lay summary at the outset, to widen their impact and accessibility to the public and patients. The overall aim is to make the results of well-conducted research readily available as a foundation stone for evidence-based medicine. On rereading *Effectiveness and Efficiency*, and also Cochrane's autobiography *One Man's Medicine*, it seems to me that naming this web-based library the 'Cochrane Library' was an entirely fitting tribute to this remarkable man, and provides an ongoing legacy for his vision and ideas. His name is now synonymous with evidence-based medicine, and he is known by doctors worldwide. There were two factors that helped to make the Cochrane Library happen: firstly, the internet was just starting to take off; secondly, a methodology had been created which allowed for the systematic and unbiased reviewing of all of the published research studies of treatments for a particular condition, termed 'systematic reviews'. Cochrane died in 1988, unaware of any of this.

Like Cochrane, I was also in my forties and in Cardiff when I found my feet in a field of research, photodermatology. By coincidence, my main research interest became a group of metabolic diseases called 'porphyria'. Archie Cochrane and many members of his family suffered from variegate porphyria, a very rare condition which can be life-threatening.

Evidence-based medicine was a concept that greatly appealed to me. It provided a methodology for a style of research I was already drawn to and had used repeatedly: to integrate the experience of the clinician and the values of the patient to systematically search the medical literature and analyse the data in an objective and independent way to create new knowledge. This was such a simple concept, so easy to grasp and understand. It also fitted well with my character and skill set, providing legitimacy and respectability to the newly created field of 'information science'. Furthermore, it complemented both laboratory science and qualitative research methods. We were to use research that embraced systematic review methodology in all of the master's degrees and medical doctorates that I was subsequently to supervise; these research projects came to define my career.

●　　●　　●

AN EIGHT-YEAR-OLD GIRL WITH BLISTERS

Rhian is just eight years old and is suffering from a blistering skin disease of childhood. She has the classic clinical features, with semi-circular lines of small blisters on the lower tummy and inner thighs. It is a very rare condition; we seek advice on management from the dermatologists at Great Ormond Street Hospital for Sick

Children. We treat her with dapsone, a drug licensed for leprosy, but sometimes used off-licence to treat skin diseases. The blisters gradually retreat, becoming less frequent. Eventually, they stop altogether. We cautiously withdraw the dapsone, and wait to see if the blisters return. They don't. The blistering disease has run its course and is no longer active. Rhian is better. Interestingly, this is anecdotal medicine working in a positive way, there being no clinical trials on this rare condition.

CHAPTER 11

A PATIENT-CENTRED APPROACH

1994–1998

I started work as a new consultant in Newport, South East Wales, in 1994. The old guard at the Royal Gwent Hospital were always happy to share their memories of how things used to be. This was medicine from another era. Most of the older doctors lived near to the hospital; had there been an emergency, they could be there in minutes. Living close to the hospital, near each other, and sharing this demanding lifestyle created a bond of kinship that ran deep.

Each year there were two dinners for the consultants and their spouses, one in the summer, another in the winter. We would gather at a local hotel in black tie for dinner and dancing. The retiring consultants were, by tradition, the guests of honour. In those days retiring doctors staggered over the finishing line, like marathon runners who have hit the wall, and are close to collapse. These evenings were friendly and collegiate, but often tinged with regret. The older consultants and their spouses were clearly nostalgic for the past when this was an event not to be missed. But the nature of these gatherings had changed. Soon, there were insufficient numbers for a dance; before long, even the dinner was poorly attended; eventually, the dinners stopped altogether.

Occasionally, the retiree would give an excellent speech: humorous, insightful, self-deprecating, and well-judged. But it was hard not to detect a note of regret in their stories. Most were clinicians whose lives had been spent conducting daily ward rounds, clinics and, for the surgeons, operating lists. Some might have done private practice to ease financial pressures, but this added to their weekly clinical workload. For them – and this is where my generation have been so lucky – research in an NHS hospital was extremely rare, with neither the infrastructure nor support from colleagues. Teaching, if they did any, was apprentice-style for the junior doctors, who worked alongside their senior colleagues to learn on the job. In those days there was minimal medical management. There was little opportunity for leadership, as most consultants were just trying not to sink under their clinical burden.

No wonder so many of them had become cynical and jaundiced about the NHS and their professional lives as doctors. They did not have the career support or opportunities that are now the norm; it was harder in their day. The speeches tended to follow a familiar pattern: reminiscences about a lost past, a golden era, would segue into how ghastly modern medicine had become, with examples to illustrate the point; bitterness about being passed over for promotion, or failing to receive support for a pet project leading to a final moan about 'management' and then the inevitable, 'Well, I must say, I don't envy those of you starting out on your consultant careers...'

There was the softly spoken chest physician with a mischievous sense of humour and a gift for words. His legendary status at the Royal Gwent Hospital was enhanced by driving a vintage Rolls Royce. He was once called to court as an expert witness on behalf of the defence and responded to the prosecution expert's testimony with the line of defence, 'His was a council of perfection rich with the benefit of hindsight.' The judge agreed, and the case was dismissed; there had been no medical negligence.

Then there was the surgeon and medical director at the Royal Gwent Hospital, whose kind eyes peering out over half-moon glasses looked less kindly upon medical blunders. When I saw him, summoned to discuss two serious incidents where patients were suing the hospital following ultraviolet light therapy burns, he was not amused.

'Once is forgivable, but twice is starting to look careless,' he said.

He made it clear that there would be no more mistakes with phototherapy and expected me to sort it out (which I did).

The two diabetes and endocrinology consultants were both raconteurs, and were much loved by their clinical teams despite their interminable ward rounds. I had arranged to meet them for a pre-interview chat and they saw me together. Both were interested in what I had to say. They encouraged me to keep going with research, saying they would support me if I was appointed. Both became friends as well as respected senior colleagues.

In time, I found my feet as a new consultant. I enjoyed the multiple roles I took on: clinical medicine, teaching, medical leadership and research; but I was careful never to lose interest in the human aspects of healthcare.

It is always about the patients.

Once established, that bond with a patient is never lost. It takes just a minute or two, and confirms them to be human beings, not anonymous patients with skin disease. Only through the human touch can one find the compassion and care that is essential for good doctoring. Perhaps it also changes the patient's perception of me, showing that I'm also a human being as well as a doctor. I suspect that doctors who lose sight of their patient's humanity and individuality end up finding medicine exhausting. These are the doctors who are relieved to retire, having had enough. Ultimately, the medicine becomes less interesting; it's the patients who are endlessly fascinating. The intellectual challenge of medicine is to help the patient in front of us, recognising that no two patients are the same. Understanding and respecting the patient's identity, their worries, their fears and their beliefs is all part of the challenge. It is not one-size-fits-all; quite the opposite. Every patient is a challenge; every clinic requires extra effort and human engagement. The upside is that doctoring can be rewarding every day.

* * *

RECURRENT ABSCESSES AND BOILS IN A RHEUMATOLOGY CLINICAL NURSE SPECIALIST AGED FIFTY-TWO

'Tell me the story in your own time,' I say. Helen is clearly upset and exasperated as she describes her last few months to me. We are sitting together in the outpatient clinic.

It started, she tells me, with a painful boil on her bottom about six months earlier. 'I never suffer with boils, so this was out of the ordinary. The GP gave me antibiotics. It was really painful to sit on, but soon discharged pus and eventually healed to create a scar.' She stands up to show me her bottom before I have time to offer her a chaperone. 'Then, two weeks later, I developed another painful abscess on my right upper arm. It was the same story. Off to the GP, more antibiotics, more pain, more pus, and another scar.' She pulls up her clothing to reveal another recent scar. 'But this was just the start of it. I have had nine further boils in the last few months. Usually one at a time, but sometimes two or three together. I feel sorry for my GP, who keeps saying that each one should be the last. Finally, in desperation, I contacted you. One of your nurses said you might see me before your morning clinic'.

'I think I know what the problem is' I tell her. 'I have seen this once before. It sounds like infection by a very aggressive strain of Staphylococcus aureus *called PVL.'*

We take skin swabs, and discuss the provisional diagnosis. I recommend that she takes time off work until this is sorted out. A few days later, the results are back: heavy growth of Staphylococcus aureus, *PVL variant. I phone Helen to tell her the news. She sounds relieved. Treatment of this highly resistant and aggressive bacterium will not be easy, but we have a plan, and Helen can finally move forward.*

CHAPTER 12

PUBLIC VS PRIVATE PRACTICE

1994-2012

Soon after being appointed as a consultant in 1994, I decided to combine my NHS work with working at the local private hospital, known unofficially as the Golden Nugget. The hospital profits were used to fund the on-site hospice run by an order of nuns. Moving into private practice, charging patients for my time and expertise, changed everything, including the relationship with the patient. Most patients were frustrated and angry about the long NHS waiting lists and many of them could not really afford to be there. Initially, I would arrive to do a clinic, and find only two or three patients had been booked in. Most patients paid by cash. All cash transactions were carried out between the patient and the consultant in the consultation room, which added a frisson to the doctor–patient interaction: on the one hand, the patient with a bundle of cash in their pocket, anxious not to make a fool of themselves by doing the wrong thing; on the other hand, the consultant, anxious not to let the patient leave without paying, but not wanting to appear avaricious.

'Make sure to make the buggers pay before they leave; if not, it's much harder to get them to pay later,' I was advised by a fellow consultant.

Every year, just as warned, I had ten or so patients on my books who hadn't paid, despite reminders to do so.

Local GPs were, once again, key to my work; this time they acted as the gatekeepers to the Golden Nugget. With just two dermatologists to choose from, it was obvious what I needed: a reputation for excellence and a good rapport with the GPs. The situation quickly improved. I knew from my time in general practice that GPs soon learn what consultants are like by listening to their patients. Consultants who are obsequious to private patients and brusque with NHS patients establish the wrong type of reputation. I was determined to be consistent, the same with patients in the private sector as in the NHS. After all, they're the same patients, and they all report back to the same GPs. I knew that excellence in my clinical practice with a focus on patient-centred care was a strong combination. The local GPs would soon hear what I was like. If my NHS patient care was excellent, my reputation would rise. Sure enough, my private practice grew quickly.

We had our own NHS inpatient ward for dermatology in Newport.

'Alex, keep the beds full. If you don't, you will lose them!'

This was essential for my success as a consultant, I was told. The unmentioned corollary: lose your beds, and you lose everything. I noted that my colleague often admitted patients for inpatient care from his private clinic, so I did the same. My colleague was old school, with a great professional reputation. Anything he was doing regarding private practice and the NHS must be fine (illustrating the importance of role models for professional behaviour). No one questioned us, and it did not occur to either of us that we were doing wrong. On reflection, we both had a sense of entitlement to the riches from private practice. We had worked hard and had put in the time to reach this sought-after stage; this was payback. In retrospect, nobody admires entitlement. Nor should they. But it's a fact of our health system that private practice and NHS practice operate alongside each other.

How did I avoid conflicts of interest? Here's a sample of my patients.

Patient A has bad eczema so comes to see me at the Thursday private clinic. They are in a bad way, and desperate (eczema makes the skin red and itchy and can be very distressing for patients, impacting on all aspects of quality of life, including sleep). I phone the ward and pass on the details.

'They will contact you as soon as a bed is available,' I say.

Admission to hospital! At last, someone is taking the patient seriously. What a relief! Smiles all round... The perfect moment to discretely ask for payment...

'That will be £150, please.'

Nervous fumbling, a look of anxiety, a wad of notes appears (patients often have no idea what they will be charged), they count it off...

'You had better check it.' (I never did, it felt personally demeaning and unprofessional to be counting cash as a doctor.)

Within a day or two, the patient with bad eczema is admitted to the NHS dermatology ward. Within a few days, their skin is better, back to normal; they are sleeping again. The patient is discharged home, with generous supplies of creams and ointments, with a six-week NHS review appointment. All of this is done openly, and transparently. The GPs are kept informed.

Patient B comes to my private practice with a skin lesion, small, nothing serious, but needs treatment. Surgical treatment in the private sector is expensive; too costly for this patient.

'I will arrange for it to be done on the NHS; you'll have to wait, but it shouldn't be too long,' I tell him. Luckily, I have my own NHS waiting lists for skin surgery, and run an efficient service with short waiting times. Within a few weeks this patient will be treated on the NHS, having paid at the outset for a private consultation.

'That will be £150, please.'

Nervous fumbling, a look of anxiety, a wad of notes appeared, he counts it off...

Not bad for a ten-minute consultation, and the patient goes home happy. It's a way of accessing the NHS via the back door.

Patient C is struggling with bad psoriasis, and needs phototherapy (ultraviolet light therapy given three times per week for up to ten weeks). Our NHS phototherapy service lacks capacity, despite my best efforts. Demand for phototherapy greatly exceeds our capacity. The NHS resources in our unit are concentrated in the ward, with the result that our community-facing services are poor or non-existent. As a consequence, the NHS phototherapy waiting list is too long. This creates an opportunity to set up a private phototherapy service to mop up demand, a private service that is patient-focused, addressing the job they needed doing: attending for phototherapy after work, with a quick turnaround time, at a convenient location with free on-site parking. I create a private photo-therapy company with two colleagues, a nurse and a medical physicist. The business is a success, but only because the NHS is failing so badly; long NHS waiting lists and inconvenient treatment arrangements (daytime only; no parking provided; patients often kept waiting for ages) are both great recruitment sergeants for this new business. Had the waiting lists gone, so too would the private practice.

Patient D has an unusual distribution for eczema, raising the possibility of contact allergy (contact allergic dermatitis, a form of eczema cause by skin exposure to a chemical to which the patient has become sensitised and is now allergic). I take the history, examine the skin and realise that special allergy tests are needed (patch tests). However, these tests are expensive and time-consuming; most private patients can't afford this test. I refer the patient for patch testing on the NHS. Once again, having seen me as a private patient, there is no need for a further NHS outpatient clinical appointment (waiting list for these appointments is typically six to twelve months, or longer). The patient is referred to the NHS for patch testing.

'Er, that will be £150 please.'

As I became more experienced, however, I was able to see things more clearly. Here was a conflict of interest, bang in the heart of our NHS service: long NHS waiting lists lead to increased private practice. My colleague and I both did private practice; there was a shared conflict of interest and no one challenging us with ethical questions or urging us to change our practice. Did we both conspire together to keep these waiting lists long? No. However, we did not do as much as we might have done to bring the waiting lists down, either. The status quo suited us. Most of our patients were not, as you can see, wealthy; far from it. We were benefitting from their misfortune.

One Friday evening I was nearing the end of a session in private practice when a lady in her early seventies came to see me. She had dry itchy skin, and had developed a stubborn variant of eczema called discoid eczema. During the history taking I asked her what work she had done: 'I was personal assistant and librarian to an academic in Cardiff.'

'Did you enjoy the work?' I asked

'Yes, very much. I really miss the feeling of being in a team and doing something worthwhile'

'What field of research was this?' I asked.

'Epidemiology,' she replied.

'Was your boss Professor Archie Cochrane?'

'Yes! Did you know him?'

'No, but I feel I know him. What was he like?'

'He was lovely!'

She brought him to life with her affectionate and personal anecdotes about his garden in Rhoose Farm House. Archie Cochrane had inherited the family Scottish tweed cloth business in the border town of Galashiels from his grandfather. Cochrane had no need to do private practice thanks to the family fortune.

•   •   •

Patient demand for private referrals fell to almost zero when we introduced Dermatology Integrated Care to North West Wales. Before long, we rarely saw patients in our NHS clinics who had already paid to consult with a dermatologist in the private sector; there were no longer waiting lists driving this demand.

My view is that consultants should be permitted to do private practice, if they choose to do so. However, those who do private practice should be excluded from becoming clinical directors of NHS services. Long NHS waiting lists are unlikely to be addressed whilst the local clinical lead also does private practice. Part of the role of clinical director should be to develop services to ensure that patients referred by GPs are seen in a timely fashion; this means tackling long waiting lists as the top priority and ensuring that the whole system dynamics are optimised to promote patient flow. Being clinical director and doing private practice are in direct conflict with each other; separation is needed. There is a conflict of interest within the NHS which remains concealed from the public, and seldom talked about. There is a general belief that this situation is acceptable because no one says that it is not.

●　●　●

MALE, THIRTY-SIX, BLACK NAIL

Aled, thirty-six, is tall and anxious. His skin disease has affected his self-confidence, which in turn has affected him 'in the bedroom department'. He is married with two children and ends up being treated with a biological therapy. The rash disappears and all is well, until I am asked to see him on an orthopaedic ward. He hadn't told me about his black toenail, which I had failed to spot during his regular clinic appointments.

'I think I dropped something on it at work,' he says. It had been black for two years.

The orthopods remove the toenail and send off a sample to the lab. It is a malignant melanoma of the nail.

Aled has trouble taking it all in. He isn't too worried about losing his toe; it's seeing a cancer specialist that worries him.

'Is it serious?' he asks.

I continue to see him. We stop the biological therapy for his psoriasis; it comes back. The oncologist gives him interferon therapy. It is awful, with bad side effects. A few months later he dies.

CHAPTER 13

BUILDING MY TEAM
1994-2015

As a new consultant I needed to create an infrastructure to support my planned research. I was joined by two senior dermatology nurses from Cardiff, Bev and Ann. Together we created a distance learning course, Practical Dermatology Nursing, writing the course manual and the student modules over a six-month period. It was exciting to create something new. We used senior dermatology nurses from around the UK as our course content advisors, a role they enjoyed as it involved enlisting them as partners in this new initiative. Our first intake of students included nurses from all over the UK. Practical Dermatology Nursing had arrived, and was coordinated from a small office in our dermatology unit in Newport, South Wales.

At the same time, we set up a course for nurses in phototherapy. This was a four-day residential course in the St Woolos Hospital phototherapy unit. The course was popular and well attended, with nurses coming from all over the UK: there was nothing to rival it elsewhere. The course generated fees and sponsorship; the academic unit was gradually expanded by appointing more administration staff. We took the training courses around the country and then abroad, responding to demand. We would respond to these invitations by scheduling training in their dermatology unit on the weekend, from the Isle of Wight to the Highlands of Scotland. We were always given a warm reception. By the end of each weekend, we had formed new professional relationships, and empowered another group of nurses who were now equipped to provide a high level of treatment.

Our database of students showed that by 2010 more than 80 per cent of the UK's dermatology departments included nurses we had trained, thereby improving patient care around the UK. No other department in the UK could compare in terms of our impact on nursing, and the practice of phototherapy. We had even trained nurses in phototherapy from Dundee, a world-famous department with the busiest phototherapy unit in the UK; it was a department that I revered.

After five years, it seemed likely we might even be able to win a highly regarded competition, UK Dermatology Team of the Year. Our entry had nurse education and teaching as its core, in addition to our early research efforts. It was satisfying to collate our entry and consider how best to present the achievements of our team. We made the final four, and were visited by the judge. We were all interviewed, explaining in detail how the nurse education courses were run, and how this teaching had impacted positively on local and national patient care.

The winner of the UK Dermatology Team of the Year for 2000 would be announced at a gala dinner and prize ceremony in the Park Lane Hotel, London. Think the Oscars, with doctors. Six of our team attended, three doctors and three nurses. We travelled together by train, tuxedos or long dresses in a suit-bag, and an overnight case for the stay in London. None of us had attended anything like this before. Early in the evening we met up, dressed in our finery. A round of drinks settled nerves, then off to the Park Lane Hotel by taxi. There were multiple categories at the awards ceremony from across medicine. The format was typical for an awards ceremony, with each shortlisted team briefly described to the audience, followed by a drum roll and the envelope opening. A BBC newscaster was the compère, with Joanna Lumley as the guest celebrity. We were sitting at the same table as a competitor team, the other two shortlisted dermatology teams on an adjacent table. We mostly knew each other, and the atmosphere was warm and friendly; after all, we were all winners in getting this far in a national competition. The awards process took ages: award after award, each with a shortlist of four teams.

Then our category was announced.

'And the Dermatology Team of the Year is...'

...we had won

I went up to receive the trophy, and said a few words to acknowledge our team. The award was a huge boost for our department. I received letters of congratulations from senior people in NHS Wales; we were suddenly on first name terms. We also made it to the *South Wales Argus*, who were generous in their praise. Everyone seemed pleased by our success, which we were told reflected well on the whole healthcare community in Wales. Our NHS organisation, the Gwent Healthcare NHS Trust, had only been created a year earlier; the new management were thrilled as this was the first national award on their watch. Trust chairman David Jessop praised our team effort for this singular achievement. Some of the non-executive board members wrote me personal letters of congratulations. Despite this, there was no time to pause and reflect on our success. The pressure to generate funds for Academic Dermatology, our small research unit, was relentless; the administration staff needed paying each month and the research costs were accumulating.

Entrepreneurship requires constant growth in order to be sustained; if we paused now to wallow in our success or simply take stock of the situation, the funds would dry up. The research was gathering pace, with a steady stream of high quality projects and publications. My partner in these research efforts was Chris Edwards, a medical physicist PhD and expert in the physics of ultraviolet. It was the ideal partnership, founded on close friendship and mutual respect; furthermore, we were both gaining from our collaboration. We complemented each other, and shared a passion for research. We were experienced at navigating this challenging landscape. We were also pragmatic, recognising the need to be focused and play to our strengths, using our limited resources wisely.

Over a fifteen-year period, our collaboration would lead to the creation and completion of five medical doctorate projects. Medical Doctorates (MDs) are research degrees at the same level as a PhD, but requiring just one year of full-time study, rather than the three years needed for a PhD. They were created to allow medical doctors to do a research degree without being excessively onerous in terms of the quantity of research and duration of the project. Although the MD research itself was just one year of full-time study, each project requires at least one year to set up and another year to write up and submit to the university.

The five doctors who completed MDs with us would have the opportunity to follow a clinical research pathway in their career: Dr Suliman Otman from Libya; Dr Omar al Ofi from Saudi Arabia; Dr Alex Holme from Scotland; Dr Ru Katugampola from England; Dr Deana al Ismail from Wales. Each had a unique area of expertise. I was particularly proud when one external examiner, a recently retired professor of dermatology from Leuven in Belgium, commented that this was the best performance by an MD student that he had ever seen.

Academic Dermatology was run by three administrators, Jane, Margaret and Viv. Jane was in her early fifties, bright, efficient. Her attributes made her an important recruit: she had a strong work ethic, dogged determination, abundant common sense, and a great sense of humour. Jane pulled everything together and made us an effective team. I was not surprised to discover that Jane's son was a medical scientist with a PhD, a professor involved in top-level research at the University of Bath. Margaret was also in her fifties, with an accent gained from growing up in Tooting, at the southern end of London's Northern Line. Margaret let slip once that she had once been a 'rocker' when younger, hanging out with bikers in South London. She was now divorced and had a severely disabled son, Daniel, who was much loved by everyone. Margaret could only work part-time, as caring for Daniel required so much of her day; she made these hours count, needing this break from her carer duties. Margaret and Viv had both been receptionists in the Bellevue Clinic, a large local GP surgery in Newport; they had worked together for a few years. Viv was a few years younger than Jane and Margaret and had grown up in Newport. She was proud of her hometown, despite it being dilapidated and a bit run-down. Viv was the only one of our team who had experienced Newport's nightlife in her younger days, including TJ's, Newport's well-respected small alternative music venue. This was the town where John Mellor made his first tentative steps towards the Rock and Roll Hall of Fame; he went on to become 'Joe Strummer', the lead singer of The Clash. Viv had been part of that same Newport scene. John Mellor had worked part-time as a gravedigger at St Woolos Cemetery (there is no historical blue plaque yet), just a couple of minutes' walk from the Academic Dermatology offices where Viv, Margaret and Jane worked as administrators at St Woolos Hospital.

Our next educational project was a new course for doctors in photodermatology, to complement an established course on the same subject area. The established course had a great reputation, but for me was too long, too scientific, too expensive and used what I thought were dull teaching methods. I spotted an opportunity to create a course that was none of these things: the new course would be two days not four, with no basic science lectures, and would be much cheaper. Our unique selling point would be significant online learning at home before attending the course. The aim was to create a course that was enjoyable, and would provide the doctors with practical knowledge and skills which they could apply to patient care in their own clinical practice; hence the name of the course, Applied Photodermatology. We used real case scenarios, expert patients, and small group discussions. This provided students with an interactive format, aimed at achieving deeper learning and understanding. But how best to create online content that was engaging for students without spending money?

Brainstorming over chocolate digestives and coffee, crammed into the central office of Academic Dermatology at St Woolos Hospital, we tried to come up with a solution to our dilemma. We knew how to use Camtasia, a new home editing software programme, to create integrated sound for PowerPoint lectures. However, the sound quality was poor, which made these short lectures feel cheap and second-rate. How could we use this technology to create something really high quality without going to the expense of a professional recording studio? Secondly, we had no money in the pot for honoraria to pay expert guest speakers. How could we get them to give their recordings free?

'How about converting the small office into a recording studio?' suggested Jane.

None of us knew what would be involved, but it sounded expensive. The meeting finished; nothing had been agreed, except to meet again a few days later.

The following week I was in the office when a bulky soft parcel arrived for Jane. A few days later she emailed to see when I could next visit the Academic Dermatology offices. That afternoon, I called in to find the walls of the small office draped with thick black felt, hanging from wooden batons screwed to the walls. The double-glazed window now had secondary glazing, creating triple glazing. On the outside of the door was a large laminated sheet of white card saying *Silence! Recording in progress*. On the desk was a large professional-looking microphone on a stand. Jane had created a recording studio.

We both listened. When we spoke to each other, or rustled some paper, the sound within the room was completely dead, all absorbed by the felt-covered walls. The only noise was external: the bustle from outside, the phone ringing, someone talking, a tea cup clinking in a saucer, the quite tap, tap, tap of fingers on a keyboard.

'Amazing! Well done Jane! I think this will work,' I congratulated her.

But who would do the recorded lectures when we had no money to pay them?

'You, of course,' she said. 'We don't have to pay you. We can all help to prepare the lectures and you can do the voiceover.'

This was another great idea that would get Applied Photodermatology launched. In time we would add to the set of recorded lectures by being opportunistic and recording lectures whenever guest speakers were in the area. Most would be intrigued by the concept of a recorded lecture, having never done one before. I would explain there was no honorarium, and their recorded lecture would be accessed by multiple delegates. Jane coordinated these recordings, and edited the soundtrack, with technical support from Nic Tarran. She had acquired the skills of a recording engineer and a sound editor. Delegates on our courses regularly asked how we could afford to create such high quality teaching material.

'Did you use a professional recording studio?'

'Yes,' I said, which was sort of true.

Necessity had forced us to be creative. The sound quality was pristine, with the exception of just one lecture by Professor Henry Lim, a high-profile academic dermatologist from the USA, and future president of the American Academy of Dermatology. If you listened carefully, on slide twelve on his third recorded lecture, you could hear 'Beep! Beep! Beep! Attention! Lorry reversing! Attention! Lorry reversing! Beep! Beep! Beep!'

Despite the triple glazing, the bin men on Friday mornings had been captured on our soundtrack.

The Applied Photodermatology course ran once yearly for nine years. By the end of nearly a decade there were sixty short recorded lectures accessible to students from six weeks before the face-to-face teaching, as pre-course learning. We scheduled the face-to-face teaching for March to coincide with the Welsh daffodils, our course logo. The feedback from students was positive, some of the best I have received as a medical educator. Students particularly liked the distance learning format, the web-based lectures, the short duration of the face-to-face teaching, and the low course fees. We complemented the other available course, which may explain why they never gave me a hard time (their course remained a success). I even used Applied Photodermatology as an opportunity to invite one of the rival course directors as a guest lecturer. Professor John Hawk greatly enjoyed the experience. He stayed at our home and met my family; we became close friends. I discovered that teaching could be a great way to bring like-minded people together, and forge friendships.

Academic Dermatology was a shared endeavour that we all believed in. The health board regularly acknowledged this success, some referring to us as the 'jewel in the crown'. I was reminded of the following:

'I swear by Apollo the physician and by Asclepius and Hygeia and Panacea and by all gods and goddesses, making them my witness, that I will fulfil according to my ability and judgement this oath and obligation: To hold him who taught me the art (of medicine) as equal to my parents and share my life with him and provide for him if he is in need; to regard his offspring as my own brothers and to teach them the Art, if they need to learn it, without fee or obligation.'

This, of course, is the Hippocratic Oath.

• • •

YOUNG FEMALE ARTIST WITH PHOTOSENSITIVITY

Jenny was eighteen when she first became sensitive to sunlight. A student on an art foundation course in Newport, she plans to become an artist. She has already sold pictures to local galleries. The sun sensitivity is striking, always in the same sequence: just a few minutes of sun exposure results in redness and wealing of exposed skin, with striking linear transition to normal skin at sites of clothing like the collar line and cuffs.

Jenny's light tests confirm the diagnosis: she has solar urticaria, a rare form of sun sensitivity characterised by urticarial wealing of sun-exposed skin within minutes of sun exposure, which fades and resolves within two to three hours of being inside out of the sun. Unfortunately, the light tests show her to be sensitive to UVB,

UVA and visible light. This means that she needs to protect her skin from daylight in winter and summer; she can only go outside safely at dusk and dawn. We try lots of different treatments, without success.

Fast-forward five years. A new biological therapy (a monthly antibody injection) has become available for severe asthma. I find reports of it being used to treat solar urticaria, with apparent success. It is expensive, but Jenny is suffering badly, depressed and deprived of the outdoors, the inspiration for her art. I ask the local immunologist to endorse my request to the hospital drugs and therapeutics committee, which he does. A couple of months later, Jenny starts her monthly injections with omalizumab. It works. Her career as an artist is back on track, her quality of life restored.

CHAPTER 14

FAITH OSIER, MEDICAL HERO

1981–2021

It was June 1981, my first time in Africa and my last backpack-ing holiday before embarking on a career in clinical medicine. My plan, such as it was, was to visit my father's cousin and her husband on their farm at Naro Moru, on the slopes of Mount Kenya; the trip would end three months later at Somerset West with my mother's sister and her husband, a few miles east of Cape

Town. In between these two fixed points, I would travel overland through Kenya, Uganda, Tanzania, Zambia, Zimbabwe, Botswana and South Africa. I was on my own, staying in cheap hotels and hostels, using public transport to travel.

Before going to Naro Moru, I planned to backpack around Kenya. That morning in Nairobi, I was exhausted, not having slept much during the overnight flight. We had landed at dawn, the airport modern, sterile and empty; Africa had not been allowed to intrude. There I was, an hour later, wandering around the city centre, with a tiny backpack and no plans. I chanced upon the most amazing, intense but soft and feminine aroma of coffee, bitter yet sweet, with undertones of vanilla. I was mesmerised and rendered powerless as I followed my nose into the coffee shop and sat down for a coffee. Jambo! Welcome to Africa, Alex.

I decided to travel down to Mombasa by train on the overnight sleeper. I had the day to kill, and wandered around aimlessly. I discovered an Indian district, with warehouses and large shops full of silks, exotic smells and spices from the East. I rested in a park, avoiding the temptation to sleep in case I was robbed or arrested for vagrancy. I also read the *Nation* and the *Daily Post Kenya*, two local newspapers. I discovered that all was not well in Kenya. Daniel arap Moi had been president for just two years, but had wasted no time in establishing an authoritarian and corrupt regime. The opposition parties were being crushed by repression and torture. The press seemed to be autonomous, and were still vocal in expressing criticism. This would soon change as the repression intensified.

That evening, I shared a four-berth sleeper compartment with fellow Brit Colin; he was in his late twenties, a mechanical engineer from Ipswich. He had spent the previous two years in Juba, southern Sudan, doing Voluntary Service Overseas. Most of his time had been spent repairing and servicing tractors and agricultural machinery. Colin was on his way to meet two friends, and to rest and recover on Kenya's beautiful coastline. He had recently suffered from a severe bout of viral hepatitis and was still recuperating. I could see that he was deeply jaundiced, stick-thin and weak. He had been lucky to survive the harrowing journey overland from Juba to Nairobi. I helped him with his bags when he climbed into our compartment; he was too weak to lift them onto the luggage racks. We got on well, so teamed up, meeting his friends in Mombasa, and then travelling up the coast together to Malindi and Lamu. Before this, I accompanied Colin, at his request, to a hospital appointment at the Coast Provincial General Hospital in Mombasa. I was transfixed by this glimpse of a different style of medicine from my experiences in the UK, and I would return to Africa less than two years later for a two-month medical elective in Zimbabwe. Colin was experienced about life in Africa and told me a tragic story of a child on his farm in Sudan dying from malaria. I took heed, following his example by always using mosquito nets over my bed at night, tucking them in carefully, and checking for small holes. I also covered myself in insect-repellent and took anti-malarial tablets throughout my trip.

●   ●   ●

Malaria is one of the biggest health issues facing humankind; more than 200 million people are infected each year, with nearly 400,000 deaths. It disproportionately affects children in sub-Saharan Africa. Research to develop a malaria vaccine has been ongoing for decades, but a breakthrough has been elusive. A vaccine approved in 2015 has relatively low efficacy, reducing infection rates by about 50 per cent in the vaccinated. The World Health Organisation target is for an anti-malarial vaccine with at least 75 per cent efficacy. In 2021, researchers from the University of Oxford reported a study on a candidate malaria vaccine with efficacy of 77 per cent over twelve months. Another promising development in August 2021 was an early report in the *New England Journal of Medicine* of a new monoclonal antibody for malaria prevention from North American researchers. Their research is still active, but their early results were impressive. The first vaccine for malaria was approved by the World Health Organisation in 2021 for use in childhood in places with transmission of Plasmodium falciparum, the deadliest of the five parasites that cause malaria, and the most common in Africa.

All doctors interested in health and healthcare in Africa follow this evolving story with great interest, none more so than Dr Faith Osier, a Kenyan doctor, now living and working in the United Kingdom as a leading medical researcher.

•   •   •

For Faith Osier, the smell of coffee on the streets of Nairobi was a familiar part of growing up in the city. The second of six children, Faith was inspired to study medicine by a female doctor friend of her mother, a strong positive role model. She studied medicine at the University of Nairobi, and then worked at the Coast Provincial General Hospital in Mombasa, the same hospital I had visited sixteen years earlier with my friend Colin.

Osier was doing a residency in surgery in Mombasa, but was emotionally traumatised by dealing with a spate of brutal and horrific injuries in autumn 1997. An inter-tribal dispute now referred to as 'the Likoni Massacres' took place in slums just outside Mombasa. Raiders targeting non-local Kenyans killed at least ten policemen and many from the Luo, Luhya, Kamba and Kikuyu communities; thirty-seven of the raiders were also killed in these violent clashes.

Osier switched to paediatrics, a discipline she found more compatible with her personality, temperament and career ambitions. In 1998, Osier moved up the coast to Kilifi District Hospital, not far from Malindi. She rented a small house on the beach, a few miles from the hospital, using this peaceful idyl to read journals, and make her first tentative efforts at writing research papers. She was struck by the suffering and high death rate from malaria in children; it was not uncommon for her to admit five children to the high-dependency unit during a busy night shift, many of whom did not survive. This had a profound effect on Osier.

'These moments inspired me to think about prevention,' she said. 'What if we could stop these children from getting malaria in the first place?'

In 2001 Osier moved to the UK to continue her paediatric training in the NHS. Working in Liverpool, she passed her paediatric exams, then switched to research, doing a master's degree in immunology at the University of Liverpool. Top of the class, Osier went on to do further research as a Wellcome Research Training Fellow. She completed her PhD in 2008. Osier's research trajectory can be mapped by her success in hunting for and finding protein structures on the malaria organism (antigens) against which human antibodies had formed naturally: one as a master's student; then six during her PhD; then thirty-six more as a post-doctoral student. Thanks to her efforts, a better understanding of the natural human immune responses to malaria has emerged which will be essential if more effective anti-malarial vaccines are to be developed.

Early in 2021, Osier said: 'There's never been a better time to be an immunologist. The entire world is acutely aware of the expertise and value we bring to help solve some of the world's most pressing health problems'.

She had just been appointed as executive director of the Human Immunology Laboratory at the not-for-profit scientific research organisation based at Imperial College London. I was filled with pride to read that Imperial, my alma mater, was now hosting such an important and charismatic research leader. In accepting this new and prestigious appointment, Osier said that she had been inspired by the global partnerships and political will which had led to the creation of effective COVID-19 vaccines. 'We must do the same for malaria,' was her view. Her mission, she said, was to energise the research community and use their collective internal expertise and global partnerships to solve this problem. If anyone is likely to make malaria history in our lifetimes, it is Osier.

I was reminded of the enormity of this challenge by memories of staying in a cheap hotel when backpacking in 1982 in Malawi. I had spent the day at Cape Maclear, a small and picturesque resort town on Lake Malawi. I left it too late to travel back to Zomba, and was forced to stay overnight in a small guest house a few miles along the road. My experience of Africa had taught me to always sleep under mosquito nets, tuck them in carefully, and check for holes. My torch might come in handy, as the room lighting was so poor. I turned out the light to go to sleep, and turned on my torch for a final check. I was not alone. The torch illuminated not just one or two, but hundreds of mosquitos; many had landed on the outside of my mosquito nets, attracted by my body heat, a few centimetres from my skin. It was too hot in the room for sheets or a T-shirt, further highlighting my sense of vulnerability. Despite avoiding any bites that night, I slept poorly, and jumped out of bed at first light, heading for the exit.

* * *

My medical elective in 1982 provided an opportunity to travel overseas as a medical student and experience healthcare in a different setting. I chose Zimbabwe and was posted to a mission hospital in the rural south-east, just a short walk from Great Zimbabwe, the ruins of a medieval stone city from which this country had taken its name. The civil war was over, and Robert Mugabe was now president. The currency was stable, the economy fairly strong, tourism was thriving, the roads were smooth and pothole-free. The government had just launched a new campaign, 'health for all by the year 2000'. What would happen in the following eighteen years was anyone's guess, but this slogan was trotted out as a form of political levelling-up. The first time I heard it, I was sitting in the shade of an acacia tree, about twenty miles from the mission hospital near Masvingo, a remote rural setting in the south-east of the country. A community nurse was speaking to a large group of mothers and children, explaining about the measles, mumps and rubella vaccinations we were there to administer. She did a great job, judging by the body language and compliance of her audience. She finished by telling them about 'health for all by the year 2000'. The audience were polite, but looked bemused. These people were living in mud huts; they had small vegetable patches, some poultry and a goat or two. The future for them did not extend much beyond tomorrow, or perhaps next week, never mind the year 2000.

I was helping with the vaccinations. This was much harder than I had anticipated. Due to shortages, there were no disposable needles and syringes. The German doctors running the local mission hospital had resorted to sterilising and reusing these single-use needles. They were all blunt, which meant the process of vaccination required an overarm stabbing motion, rather than the more conventional underarm slide-it-in gently technique; significant force was needed to penetrate the skin. This made the vaccinator (me) appear to be barbaric; it was also clearly very painful for the poor children. The only people who gained from this experience were the already vaccinated older children who had come to see the fun. Their faces lit up as their two-year-old brothers and sisters were delivered to the tall white medicine man to be stabbed in the bum with a blunt syringe. How they screamed! How their siblings laughed!

The German doctors were an inspiration – so dedicated to their cause, and uncomplaining about the long hours and insatiable demand for healthcare. They had a large textbook of medicine as practiced in remote rural locations in Africa: how to diagnose and treat trachoma (an eye disease spread by flies which leads to blindness if untreated); how to remove a cataract; how to do a caesarean section; how to give a general anaesthetic. On one occasion I witnessed a doctor giving a general anaesthetic, handing airway control to an assistant, and then doing a caesarean section.

One day I accompanied Joerg, one of the doctors, to see a patient. We drove for about an hour, down dirt tracks, bumping our way along whilst raising a huge plume of dust behind the Land Rover. We eventually came to a small community building, made from mud-bricks, with a corrugated metal roof. It was a community pharmacy and health centre, a distant outpost of the mission hospital. The woman we were there to see looked at us suspiciously, with wide, staring eyes. She hardly spoke, responding to questions with occasional nodding of the head, or dismissive hand signals. She reminded me of a woman with post-natal depression I had seen a few months earlier at the West London Hospital (the same hospital where the young Archie Cochrane had worked as a junior doctor). Severe depression appeared to have exactly the same outward manifestations in rural Africa as in London. Joerg was kind and sympathetic, his words a soothing balm, his advice helpful and pragmatic. He made recommendations to the medical officer and left some strong prescription drugs; we would be back the following week to assess her progress, he explained. On the return journey to the mission hospital Joerg told me about the stigma of mental health in this community. The woman had been cast out, her mental demons making her unwelcome to her family and her village; a person to be feared.

•   •   •

In 2005, I was fortunate to have the opportunity to take a sabbatical in Cape Town, South Africa. Three months away was a chance to recalibrate and to take stock; it was a time of reflection. My trip to South Africa made me reassess my practice, the UK and my priorities for the next few years. My wife Sarah and our children Becca and Ben joined me for two months, as it coincided with the UK summer holidays. It was winter in Cape Town, wild storms rolling in from the ocean, interspersed with cold, clear, sunny days of calm. We were able to rent an amazing apartment for not very much; it was off-season and demand for apartments was low.

South Africa was still in transition following the end of apartheid in 1994. Thabo Mbeki had replaced Nelson Mandela as president in 1999. Six months before my visit, Nelson Mandela had announced his retirement from public life. I arrived in Cape Town in June 2005 and was greeted with political turmoil. The papers were full of scandals and accusations concerning Jacob Zuma, the leading candidate in the upcoming presidential election. Almost daily, I read newspaper reports of new scandals. Zuma need not have worried; like Boris Johnson in the UK in 2018, he had charisma, and was elected to replace Thabo Mbeki in a landslide victory. However, in contrast to both of his predecessors, Zuma lacked integrity, and was corrupt. Those pre-election scandals were the warning that the electorate chose to ignore.

The Groote Schuur Hospital, where the world's first heart transplant was performed in 1967, included a dusty museum on the ground floor dedicated to this event. I vividly remembered this story from the TV news of my childhood. The heart of a young mixed-race girl killed in a car accident just outside the hospital had been used to replace the failing heart of an elderly white male. Now I was shocked to realise that these events had taken place during the era of apartheid, when there were still whites-only park benches and whites-only beaches.

I discussed Christiaan Barnard, the pioneering heart-transplant surgeon, with my new colleagues at Groote Schuur Hospital and was disappointed to hear that his legacy had been small. In contrast to the doctors, scientists and politicians who would inspire me throughout my career, Christiaan Barnard was a flawed character who was seduced by fame and celebrity. As a brilliant surgeon he had failed to commit to academia, his research output modest at best. In contrast to Jenner, Osler, Osier, Cochrane, Christensen, Berwick and Tudor Hart, he failed to recognise the doing was just a small part of medical progress; the writing-up was just as important.

I was based on the top floor of Groote Schuur Hospital in the porphyria unit, supervised and hosted by two professors, both porphyria experts. One was a clinician (he saw patients), the other a scientist (he was lab-based and tended not to see patients). Both were generous with their time and passionate about porphyria research; they had established an international reputation for their unit, which was why I was there. I saw many patients with the variant of porphyria that was so common in South Africa, and quickly became familiar with the diagnosis and management of this disorder. Variegate porphyria was characterised by a blistering skin rash caused by sensitivity to sunlight (hence my interest in this disorder, as I was a photo-dermatologist) as well as occasional, acute, life-threatening attacks. This was a condition that could kill you, so the diagnosis and management were important. It had become common in South Africa due to a so-called 'founder effect'. That is, one person carrying the dodgy gene had arrived in the closed community of Dutch settlers, the Afrikaners. This in itself would not have been enough. The crucial ingredient for a founder effect was generation after generation of fecundity: huge families and a small gene pool ensured that variegate porphyria became established and common in the Cape community of Dutch settlers. There are now an estimated 10,000 people in South Africa with variegate porphyria, and about 30,000 who carry the dodgy gene. This equates to an incidence in South Africa of one case per 300 unaffected in the population. In contrast, the rate is one case per 300,000 in the UK.

I wrote a detailed and complex review article on porphyria in this three-month period, which was published in a high-ranking journal soon after my return to the UK. I returned to the NHS and to academia refreshed and reinvigorated and was delighted to be appointed as honorary professor of dermatology by Cardiff

University. It was important for me. Now all I had to do was to live up to the title.

• • •

INTENSIVE CARE UNIT,
GROOTE SCHUUR HOSPITAL

He looks like a child; small and frail. I was told that the tattoos on his arms are those of an infamous local gang. I read on his medical record that he is aged forty-three. He is on a ventilator, drugs to support his cardiac output, a pacing wire to keep the heart beating.

A regular patient to this intensive care unit, he chooses to ignore advice to avoid taking recreational drugs. This is his third admission this year, and it is only June. It isn't the drugs themselves which have caused him to be admitted; they have triggered an acute porphyria crisis, characterised by shutdown of the autonomic nervous system for a few days. The autonomic nervous system keeps us breathing, the heart beating and the guts and bowel moving; shutdown leads rapidly to death without intervention and support. This is the life-threatening part of variegate porphyria, which can be prevented by avoiding drugs that precipitate these crises. Much of my time in the Cape Town porphyria clinic has been spent educating patients on how to avoid these acute crises; recreational drugs are top of the forbidden list. Nearly all patients take this advice seriously, most avoiding these life-threatening episodes altogether.

Two days later he is off the machines. He has something to eat and then discharges himself.

CHAPTER 15

LLOYD GEORGE'S LEGACY

1863-2019

The statue of David Lloyd George (1863–1945) that stands in Caernarfon's main square was unveiled when he was still prime minster. It was a statue I was familiar with from taking visiting friends and family to see Caernarfon Castle. I could also sing the First World War marching song ('Lloyd George knew my faaather, father knew Lloyd George...') thanks to my father humming it when we went on long walks together. But that was it. I knew little more about David Lloyd George, the only Welsh man to become prime minster. One day after work, having driven to a cottage hospital just outside Pwllheli, through the Caernarfon constituency he had served for fifty-five years, I decided that rather than pass the sign, 'Turn left at next junction for Llanstumdwy, The Lloyd George Museum', I would pay it a visit. I knew that his efforts as a politician had helped usher in the creation of the welfare state. I now wanted to understand the man behind the UK government's introduction of a national scheme for insurance against sickness, unemployment and invalidity, with contributions levied on the workers and their employers, and subsidised by the state.

'You haven't got long,' said the lady in the museum.

I paid the entrance fee, bought a guide book and headed through the museum towards a woodland to see the monument erected to commemorate Lloyd George.

The architect who had designed the monument, Clough Williams-Ellis, was also responsible for creating the Italianate Portmeirion village, and other architectural gems in the area.

Clough Williams-Ellis and David Lloyd George had been good friends, both being local celebrities. It was Clough who had renovated the farmhouse that David and his second wife Fanny had purchased in 1942 next door to Brynawelon, the house Lloyd George had shared with his first wife Margaret and their five children. They moved in two years later, only for Lloyd George to die the following year. Fanny commissioned Clough Williams-Ellis to create a monument to her husband around the grave he had chosen, next to his beloved River Dwyfor.

I had the place to myself. I admired the ornate iron entrance gate, set in a stone wall, unmistakably in the style of Clough

Williams-Ellis. A porthole-like circular opening above the gate included more ironwork, with David Lloyd-George's initials. On the other side of the wall was an englyn (a short strict-metre poem in Welsh) engraved in slate, composed by Lloyd George's nephew William George: 'The rough stone and the stone of his crown – is the grave of a man who was a hero to his people; Merry Dwyfor is a beautiful watercolour, that continuously embraces the grave.'

The burial monument consisted of an oval enclosure with a large stone centred over the grave, sitting on a semi-circular plinth of pebbles from the beach at Criccieth. He used to sit on this stone. It was huge, much larger than any rock nearby. No wonder he wanted to be buried here.

I was curious: how had he made the leap from this rural backwater in Wales, to becoming one of the most powerful and influential prime ministers in our history?

A few weeks later, I met Dafydd Williams, a volunteer at the David Lloyd George Museum. Dafydd explained to me that Lloyd George had grown up as a boy in Criccieth, before becoming a trainee solicitor just down the road in Porthmadog. His childhood had featured profound hostility between the English Church and the Welsh people. This was a rural farming community; in those days agricultural rents included tithes, paid by local farmers to support the English priesthood. This issue gave a moral dimension to the Welsh religious revival which had started in the 1850s. The resentment and injustice of these tithes was a cause waiting for a champion. The English landowner's arrogance and spite towards the Welsh was exemplified by John Parry, land agent to the local squire, who famously turned out sixty-eight tenant farmers after the defeat of the Conservative candidate in the 1868 election.

David George lost his father to TB when he was aged just eighteen months. Into this void had stepped his mother's brother, Richard Lloyd. Richard had a small shoemaking business. For the devout Richard, caring for his sister and her three children was a calling from God. He never married, and dedicated everything to this task. It was fortunate, for Lloyd George's mother Betsy was not a strong woman. It soon became apparent to Richard that the young David was a truly extraordinary boy, a 'prodigy'. Richard acknowledged his devotion to the boy by adding an unhyphenated 'Lloyd' to his name, Richard's own surname. Thus he had both his father's and his uncle's names.

The National School at Llanystumdwy recognised neither the Welsh language, nor any religion other than Church of England. In contrast, Welsh was the language spoken in the George and the Lloyd families; religious life, also conducted in Welsh, was held at the local Baptist church at Penymaes. In other words, all social intercourse was in Welsh, except for school. The three school governors were English: the local squire, another local land owner and the Anglican Bishop of Bangor.

I wondered how this tension had affected the young David when the pupils were 80 per cent non-conformist. In other words, most of the pupils were like David and came from families who attended Welsh denomination churches. Aged fifteen, David was the instigator of a silent rebellion, where the pupils had planned a protest of silence for the visiting school inspector when they were asked to recite the Creed in English. Whenever the opportunity arose, David resisted authority; he was a natural rebel. He wanted to control events himself rather than assume a passive role, as was expected of the Welsh at that time.

David found childhood Baptist prayer meetings dull and repetitive but took refuge in the spoken word, captivated by preachers who were able to look the members of the congregation in the eye and connect with them emotionally. His first political motive was to speak up for the Welsh people. Through this, he became the champion of the oppressed. It was then just a small step to fight on behalf of the downtrodden and dispossessed, the poor across the whole of the United Kingdom. This was to play out in his politics and underpin his powerful rhetoric.

He entered parliament in 1890 by narrowly winning a by-election to become the Member of Parliament for Caernarfon Boroughs, a seat he retained for fifty-five years. Appointed as Chairman of the Board of Trade, a role he was to excel in, he was then appointed as Chancellor of the Exchequer, one of the Great Offices of State and a key position of power in the Cabinet. Lloyd George was a Liberal, but had become increasingly concerned about the rise of the new Labour Party. Both parties were vying for the same voters, potentially splitting their electorate to let in the Conservatives. His first big success was the Old Age Pensions Act of 1908. This established the old age pension for the first time. However, he was quick to realise that this was not enough, addressing just one social issue, when there were many more. Lloyd George's idea was for more generous funding for social support from taxation, the benchmark and model being the system in Germany. This was not only a moral imperative for Lloyd George; it was political too. Winston Churchill, himself a radical Liberal, had warned in March 1908 that the Liberal Party must address social issues or face electoral oblivion. Lloyd George and Churchill were in agreement.

Lloyd George, man of the people, duly announced the forthcoming 'People's Budget' as 'the greatest day in his life'. He said that he was proud to be fighting the battles of class on behalf of the people from where he himself had sprung. As Chancellor of the Exchequer, he was using taxes as the engine for social policy. This People's Budget was anathema to the majority of the House of Lords, most of whom were Conservative. However, by convention, peers did not reject government budgets. Thus, peers had an unpalatable choice: accept a fiscal programme which they hated, or ignore one of the conventions of Britain's unwritten constitution. They chose the latter, leading to a constitutional crisis.

Lloyd George remained convinced that his People's Budget was a vote winner. If there was to be a constitutional crisis, and parliament was dissolved, Lloyd George believed that the Liberals would emerge from a subsequent election as the strongest party. When the budget was rejected by a huge majority in the House of Lords in November 1909, the peers proposed subjecting the bill to the judgement of the people. In other words, a general election; which the Liberals then won, but only just. The Liberals were able to form an alliance with smaller parties to create a significant majority. The People's Budget was finally passed into law in April 1910.

The inappropriate use of veto by the peers was then recognised as an anomaly in the constitution that needed correcting. This was done by the Parliament Act of 1911, which formally removed the right for peers to amend or defeat finance bills. Amid much acrimony, the bill was finally passed in the summer of 1911. The

Lords had been tamed, with Lloyd George a central figure. He had resisted authority in a determined and bloody-minded way, and had prevailed.

These bills ushered in the creation of the welfare state, funded by taxation of the rich and landed. The UK soon acquired a national scheme for insurance against sickness, unemployment and invalidity, with contributions levied on the workers and their employers, and subsidised by the state. Without this broad social policy of support for the elderly, the poor, the unemployed, the disabled and the sick it was inconceivable that the NHS would have been created. In other words, these far-reaching reforms set the scene and were the prelude to that second great social advance, the creation of the NHS in 1948.

Without Lloyd George, you don't get Nye Bevan.

* * *

MALE, AGE FORTY-SIX, PROGRESSIVE SCARRING RASH ON FACE

Consultations with Morgan are always hard work, which is why I encourage him to come at the end of the clinic. He is huge: six feet five and nearly twenty stone. He has thick, luxuriant hair which he wears long, and a neatly trimmed beard.

'I'm emotionally unstable,' he informs me. 'I think I'm having a mid-life crisis. The scarring on my face is getting worse, and it's doing my head in.'

I examine him carefully and rummage through his hair, examining his scalp, face and beard areas.

Discoid lupus can be a terrible condition, often more devastating than the multi-system variants of lupus. It is now affecting his nose, left cheek, neck, right shoulder and three separate areas in the scalp. The active disease is psoriasis-like, consisting of scaly inflammatory plaques; adjacent skin shows prominent scarring. There is patchy hair loss in the scalp and beard areas as the legacy of previous plaques.

'What do you suggest?' he asks. Treatment is proving to be difficult, as every drug I have prescribed produces unacceptable side effects: nausea with hydroxychloroquine; blurred vision with mepacrine; bad dreams with mycophenolate; deranged liver function tests with methotrexate; upset tummy and diarrhoea with azathioprine. His background anxiety ensures that discussions about each new treatment are lengthy and detailed. 'Is there anything else I can try?' he asks, sounding a bit desperate. I know that thalidomide is sometimes effective in discoid lupus, where other drugs have failed. However, the side effect profile, particularly irreversible nerve damage, rule it out for Morgan. We will have to try a different approach. 'Well...' I say, 'there is always tacrolimus ointment...'

CHAPTER 16

THE GREAT NYE BEVAN

1901–2021

In October 2009 our healthcare organisation changed its name from Gwent Healthcare NHS Trust to Aneurin Bevan University Health Board. Our catchment area included Tredegar, where Nye Bevan was born and grew up, and Ebbw Vale, the constituency he represented from 1929 until his death in 1960. My NHS patient catchment area included the whole of the Ebbw Vale parliamentary constituency. I therefore found myself serving the very same community that had given us the politician who founded the NHS, Nye Bevan. Bevan was Tredegar through and through, having been born there, then working as a miner at Ty Trist Colliery. He went on to become the local MP, and retained this role for thirty-one years. His most senior position as an MP was Minister for Health. What a journey, from teenage coal miner to one of the Great Offices of State.

But my own story of Tredegar begins in 1994, when I was one of just two dermatologists providing dermatology services in Gwent, a population of nearly 500,000. My job was peripatetic, visiting the local community hospitals for clinics and seeing hospital inpatients when requested. My first clinic was in Ebbw Vale Cottage Hospital, a long drive from my home in Cardiff, through valleys and towns familiar to me from L. S. Lowry paintings hanging in the National Museum Wales in Cardiff. On arrival, I was greeted by Sister Myfanwy Jones, my clinic nurse, with a cup of tea in a china cup and saucer. This was healthcare from another era, the visiting doctor treated like a demi-god. Everyone was friendly, but I felt uncomfortable with such deference, which I had assumed was long gone. A few miles up the road was Tredegar General Hospital, a rambling red brick building on the edge of Tredegar. There were fifty-eight beds, far more than I had expected from the small buildings visible from the road. Although badly in need of renovation and repair, it was clean and the care appeared to be good. When I visited, there were always plenty of nurses and the atmosphere was upbeat. It was all care of the elderly.

That first clinic at Ebbw Vale Cottage Hospital was straightforward. Most of the patients had minor skin problems. Most of what I saw was the sort of dermatology the local GPs should have been doing themselves. One patient would need to attend the local district general hospital in Abergavenny for ultraviolet light therapy. She agreed, and seemed content with this plan. However, when I later found out that she didn't drive, which meant she would have to go by bus, I realised it was important to find out this background information. I had given no consideration to the logistics involved for her in attending for treatment at the larger hospital. Sister Jones was part of the community and knew most of the patients by their first names; she would now be my guide with these patients.

When the clinic was over I drove home, and wondered about the background to this small but friendly cottage hospital.

It turned out that Ebbw Vale Cottage Hospital was significant as the first miner's hospital in this part of the South Wales Valleys. Commissioned in 1900, it was created by joining together two large semi-detached houses, one belonging to the local steelworks manager, the other belonging to the steelworks doctor. Importantly, this concept of a local community hospital was then replicated across the South Wales Valleys. There were five others in my patch: Tredegar Park Cottage Hospital; Redwood Memorial Hospital in Rhymney; Caerphilly Miners Hospital; Abertillery and District Hospital and Aberbargoed Hospital. In time, I was to see patients in all six of these hospitals, which sadly, having been underfunded for decades, were decrepit and earmarked for closure. In their day, these hospitals had been flagships and part of a vibrant local economy.

It was a certain Lord Tredegar who had funded the creation of these miner's hospitals, as well as the main hospitals to serve Newport and Cardiff. He had given a parcel of land to the Newport Corporation the land on which the Newport and Monmouthshire Hospital was built. Opened in August 1901, the name changed to the Royal Gwent Hospital in 1913. Lord Tredegar also opened Aberbargoed Hospital in 1909, another miner's hospital, as well as helping to fund the building of the Cardiff Royal Infirmary, which opened in 1911.

I was intrigued by Godfrey Morgan, the man behind the title, his extraordinary life connecting the era of the tragic and costly Crimean War (where he saw action) to the origins of the UK's NHS, with the investment in local hospitals. He had lived in Tredegar House, a beautiful seventeenth-century red brick country house set in ninety acres of country park on the western edge of Newport. He was regularly called upon to talk about the Charge of the Light Brigade, which apparently he did, albeit with personal modesty and regret. He tended to gloss over the tragic side of the war in the Crimea. It was hard for him to talk about, as so many of his fellow officers and men had been killed in this debacle. It was also a recognition that the reality of war was grim and not something that most people wanted to hear or could relate to.

Tredegar's involvement with setting up and opening hospitals came much later in his life. The first record of it is a fundraising speech he gave extolling the need to build a large hospital in Newport. He was ambitious that it should be large enough for Newport's rapidly growing population: 'We are met to endeavour to raise sufficient money to erect a hospital or infirmary worthy of the town of Newport. There are two statements nobody can dispute: Newport is a large and yearly increasing seaport, and a town of this magnitude ought not be without a large and splendid hospital.'

Later in the same speech in 1896, Godfrey showed that he had some insight into how hospitals operated: 'A hospital is a high school of medicine for young doctors, who not only mix with scientific people at the institution, but gain a high moral feeling, so that there is no room for petty jealousies amongst the medical practitioners.'

He also mentioned nurses: 'Then, again, a hospital makes an excellent school for nurses. That is one of the greatest benefits possible, because the authorities of the hospital are always strictly careful that nurses, before they are sent out, are thoroughly proficient.'

He concluded: 'I hope, in addition to the land, to be able to give a good sum of money if I see it is required.'

It took an enlightened individual inspired by his earliest experiences of hospitals in the battlefields of the Crimea to want to transform society, and with it people's lives. This might also explain Godfrey's surprisingly enlightened views about the place of women in society. Another of his speeches from 1900 was on the occasion of the reopening of a local private school for girls, in Cardiff:

'Women exercise a great deal of influence upon the affairs of the country, even taking part in business, politics, or anything of that sort. For all I know, there may be some girls here who will effect political and many other movements in connection with the welfare of the nation. Girls ought to be made to think that they will have a great power in the future.'

Following the success of Ebbw Vale Cottage Hospital, the Tredegar Medical Aid Society was set up to raise funds and manage the building of the hospital. Unlike Ebbw Vale Hospital, which was a fairly simple matter of creating one building from two, this hospital was built from scratch. The money for the building was cobbled together from various sources, mostly the Tredegar Iron and Coal Company, but also donations from other local companies. The hospital opened its doors to patients in 1904, with running costs paid for by the miners themselves. This was excellent health care provided on the doorstep of the local community, and paid for by that same community. *The Citadel*, a novel by A. J. Cronin about a young Scottish doctor, is based on the author's experiences of working in this hospital in the 1920s; it went on to become a bestseller, and a Hollywood and Bollywood film.

Even greater fame was then bestowed on this humble hospital. It was being involved with Tredegar Hospital that sparked the imagination of Nye Bevan, and started him thinking about using this model of healthcare nationally. Nye Bevan was a member of the Tredegar Cottage Hospital Management Committee in the late 1920s, shortly after A. J. Cronin had been working there. He ended up as chairman of the hospital management committee for two years. It was this experience which persuaded Bevan that if it was possible to provide excellent health care for the poorest communities, based on a self-funding model, then it must be possible to do the same nationally, based on taxation.

Bevan gave up chairmanship of the hospital management committee once he was elected as the MP for Ebbw Vale and

Tredegar. He was fired up by his experience of healthcare in this humble community hospital. It was some time before Bevan could do anything about it, but this was his experience of healthcare; a self-funding model which worked, that inspired his determination to roll out a similar scheme nationwide.

Bevan understood the importance of power. 'Without power, you are ineffectual,' he wrote in his 1952 book of essays, *In Place of Fear: A Free Health Service.* He continued: 'My concern was with the one practical question: where does power lie in this particular state of Great Britain, and how can it be attained by the workers?' On joining the local district council, Bevan was disappointed to discover that he did not have the sort of access to power he was after; he was told that power had shifted to the county council. He was duly elected to the county council, but again found that there was no real power there either. He then sought it by being elected into parliament, but again found that true power was in the hands of a small number of ministers, not with back benchers. He was interested in power, not for power's sake, but as an instrument of change. He wanted to improve the lives of working people. In this respect, he was very similar in outlook to David Lloyd George, with their determination to represent their own class of working people. The two men also, importantly, had an instinctive grasp of how to use power once they were in a position of influence.

A landslide Labour victory in the general election of July 1945 saw Nye Bevan appointed as Minister for Health in Clement Attlee's post-war government. Attlee anticipated significant resistance to the creation of the NHS from within the ranks of his own party, as well as from the British Medical Association, who were representing the doctors. He regarded Nye Bevan as someone with the strength, determination and zeal to win these battles and to create the National Health Service. Attlee's style was to give his ministers free rein so that they could get on with their jobs without being micromanaged, which was ideal for Bevan. Like Lloyd George, Bevan did not like being told what to do. When left to his own devices, he was very effective at resolving issues and making things happen.

The first stage of the process was fairly easy for Bevan; the National Health Service Act was passed by a huge majority in the House of Commons in May 1946. This reflected the consensus across political parties about the need to create a national health service, but not the form that it would take. Bevan was then faced with two major issues: firstly, whether to nationalise the hospitals; secondly, whether or not the doctors would be full-time salaried professionals. Bevan's idea was to create a National Health Service that would belong to the taxpayer. All hospitals would be nationalised, and the only separate class of hospital would be for teaching. The NHS would become a centralised organisation, with fourteen regional boards appointed by the Minister for Health and local management committees.

Bevan rode out the inevitable resistance to this plan. Resistance within the Cabinet was strong, but was eventually defeated by Bevan's determination, the strength of his arguments, and the support of Prime Minister Clement Attlee. The local authorities were themselves divided on these plans for a National Health Service, and chose to take their lead from the London County Council, who opted to accept the proposals. This fairly swift victory on the issue of nationalising the hospitals was followed by a much more challenging war of attrition with the British Medical Association, the union negotiating with the government on behalf of the doctors.

Bevan was strong and combative in his negotiations with the BMA; this generated friction and technical questions which threatened to bog down the negotiation process. According to Bevan's biographer Nicklaus Thomas-Symonds: 'On the Wednesday, the second day, Bevan's tone had altered. He was now handling the meeting in a very different way. His themes were reassurance and conciliation, the aggressive tone gone. He was a great tactician. He said that while voluntary hospitals would be taken over, private nursing homes would not. He also tried to calm fears of a full-time salaried medical profession. There would not be one single salary as such. There would still be an opportunity for private income.'

The BMA continued to give Bevan a rough ride in these intense face-to-face negotiations. By the close, Bevan's tone had changed from strong and determined to pleading. The BMA were holding out, and resisting the plans. Bevan decided that the best course was to go over the heads of the BMA and appeal directly to the individual doctors. He believed that the government should adhere to the set date for introducing the NHS, and should make it clear that those doctors who did not sign up would lose their present income, and their right to a share of the compensation scheme that had been set up for partnerships. The Cabinet considered this and agreed to a course of no further compromise, although it was also agreed that more would be done to explain the government's position. It was an acrimonious period, with the BMA and Bevan at loggerheads. By now the date for implementing the NHS was set, and the government were not shifting.

It was then, in April 1948, that Bevan made vital small concessions in a speech to the House of Commons: 'The Royal College of Physicians has made a useful suggestion, with which the other Royal Colleges associate themselves... My colleagues and I accept that, most cordially.' In the next BMA plebiscite of members, enough doctors were in favour of the NHS to meet the 5 July deadline. Bevan's strategy – his life's work, as it would become known – had been successfully implemented into national life.

More than sixty years after Nye Bevan died, and over seventy years since the foundation of the NHS, I was after the real story, the real Bevan; the man as remembered by his local community. I wanted to walk the same streets and visit his childhood home and school, and stand on that windy hilltop from where he announced to the world his plans to create a national health service. Unfortunately, both his childhood home and school had gone, victims of progress. But there was still plenty to see on the Nye Bevan Heritage Tour.

It was May 2021. My guide was Phillip, a local who had grown up and worked in Tredegar all of his life. Phil was introduced to me by one of my patients who lived locally. I had asked her to whom I should speak to learn more about Nye Bevan, and Phil was suggested as a local Nye Bevan enthusiast. At sixteen most of Phil's contemporaries had opted to be coal miners; Phil chose plastering and was now in his late fifties. His friend and contemporary Liam was nearly killed aged eighteen in a mining accident. He and Phil exchanged loud waved greetings from across the square:

'Sut wyt ti?' (How are you?)

'Dwi'n iawn diolch.' (I'm fine, thanks.)

'Cymer ofal butt.' (Take care, mate.)

Liam was severely disabled from the mining accident, unable to work again, but pieced together and sustained by care from the local NHS at the time of his accident and in later life.

I asked Phil about a story I had heard about Nye Bevan coming back to Tredegar for his weekly constituency surgeries. It has been said that he would leave his ministerial car parked in Newport, to avoid making the wrong impression with the locals in Ebbw Vale and Tredegar.

'It's true,' Phil told me. 'He was aware that amongst so much poverty, turning up in a flashy ministerial car would have gone down badly. He was right; it would have. In those days, not many people could afford cars, never mind flashy cars. He remained authentic, connected to his roots and his working-class origins. I think it was as much for his own benefit as for the benefit of others.'

'What do you mean by that?' I asked.

'He would have felt uncomfortable and disconnected from his origins. He wanted to remain true to the people who trusted him and had voted for him, and not appear to be gaining unduly from that support.'

On my way home I reflected on our discussions. Of course, today Nye Bevan would have been framed on social media as a hypocrite, or some such thing, but I still loved this story. How far he had come from his working class origins. The story of his ministerial car was an example of the tension he would have felt between his public and private persona. I also loved the conviction of Nye Bevan. Yes, he was hot-headed; yes, he sometimes fired off cruel and offensive tirades, when he should have remained quiet; yes, he was paranoid and attacked others, always on the front foot; yes, he quit his job as Minister for Health too soon, resigning on a matter of principle, rather than seeing the job through. Nevertheless, I loved his passion, his sense of responsibility to his origins, and his drive to address the social injustice which was all around him. How badly we need that drive and determination now, in 2022, as the NHS totters on the brink of disaster.

*   *   *

A FIFTY-TWO-YEAR-OLD WOMAN WITH ULCERS AND SCARS ON THE BREASTS

Gwen is an enigma. In her early fifties, she works at the local pension office as an administrator. She has multiple ulcerated areas on both breasts, sparing the nipples, which take weeks to heal. She already has numerous unsightly scars. I feel sure of the diagnosis at her first attendance in clinic. She is strangely indifferent to her skin disease, despite its severity. Her breasts are covered in ulcers; some are infected, with a bad odour; the rest of her skin is clear. There is no skin disease which has these features, except for dermatitis artefacta – self-imposed skin damage where the patient fails to tell the doctors what they are doing. In most cases, we don't need to be told; the diagnosis is obvious.

How was she damaging the skin? I would never know; perhaps with pliers or a kitchen knife?

The standard approach for dermatitis artefacta is to do some tests, including a skin biopsy, to rule out so-called 'organic disease' (such as a chronic, inflammatory scarring skin disorder). Confronting the patient with the diagnosis is not helpful; the patient typically denies it, and the consultation ends badly. More rewarding is to try to understand the psychopathology; what's going on in the background? In Gwen's case it was prostitutes; lots of them. Every time her pharmaceutical representative husband was away, he was at it. Gwen didn't mind too much, as long as he didn't try it on with her when he was home. 'The problem is,' she said, 'he has a "big appetite".'

'What's wrong with yer skin?' he asked her once. 'The dermatologist isn't sure,' she replied. 'He's done lots of tests, but it still isn't clear. He says the dressings mustn't be disturbed, or it will get worse. I'm going to see him again next month so he can assess my progress.'

CHAPTER 17

THE IMPORTANCE OF RESEARCH

1990-2015

My research was gathering momentum. I had chanced upon the mechanism for severe drug toxicity with azathioprine, a drug that had been prescribed for decades; this resonated throughout dermatology. To have a science-based explanation for this toxicity made clinicians sit up and take notice. There was an important patient safety issue at stake with a simple laboratory test which could detect patients who were vulnerable to this severe side effect. Without the test, the danger was severe suppression of the bone marrow leading to a life-threatening fall in the white cell count (white cells are important in fighting infection; low white cell count renders patients vulnerable to severe bacterial infections and sepsis). My publications on this niche topic of azathioprine toxicity started to accumulate.

In due course I was asked by my professional association to lead a small team in writing a clinical guideline on the use of azathioprine in dermatology. This was the first clinical guideline from the British Association of Dermatologists relating to a drug. It was also the first drug for which our professional association published an online patient information leaflet. Clinical guidelines emerged in the 1990s as an instrument for raising standards in healthcare, based on a review of the literature and expert opinion, and became an important work stream for our professional body. It was exciting to see my academic efforts noted by others, and humbling to realise that our recommendations would be heeded by clinicians throughout the world. We carefully considered the issue of pre-testing patients for susceptibility to massive bone marrow suppression with azathioprine. There was not yet sufficient evidence to support mass screening of patients prior to prescribing azathioprine; furthermore, the blood test was not yet widely available in the NHS. But we raised this issue and provided details of UK laboratories that could offer this test.

The final authorship meeting was at Willan House, the headquarters for the British Association of Dermatologists in London's Fitzroy Square. We were now leading the way on this topic, and I was lucky to have two highly respected colleagues as co-authors. We agreed on the final draft of the publication, and went our separate ways, knowing that in a few months' time this clinical guideline would be published in the *British Journal of Dermatology*, and dermatologists throughout the world would be taking on our recommendations – the result of years of research and great teamwork.

* * *

Dermatology in Cardiff in the early 1990s was an opportunity to take stock. Here the department felt like a family, safe and

supportive for trainees who were guided by experienced dermatologists. Importantly, this department had critical mass. It was
stimulating to be in such a large and dynamic team, with a wide
range of research activities. I soaked it up, learning about research
and how best to do it. I soon discovered that research required
clarity of purpose and a professional team approach. Research
also required funding, but grants were hard to obtain, tending
to go to those with a record of success. I spent the next few years
completing my clinical training, and observing how research was
done. I did small research projects, and kept publishing.

Perhaps the most important lesson I was to learn from my
time as a junior dermatologist in Cardiff in the early 1990s was
the concept of running research and education as commercial
enterprises. The professorial head of department was an academic
entrepreneur. He was successful at attracting money to pay for
his departmental research. I observed how to be professional in
setting up and running clinical trials. Participation in these clinical trials generated money for our department which was needed
to pay the salaries of academic staff, and to keep the academic
department afloat. This was my first experience of participating
in randomised controlled trials. These studies were set up and
funded by large pharmaceutical companies. They were typically
multi-centre, which meant that our unit in Cardiff was just one
of many in the UK and in Europe doing exactly the same trial.

This was also an important time for my family. My wife Sarah
and I moved to Cardiff with our baby Becca. It was a period of
consolidation and learning, building up a large network of close
colleagues and friends. Additionally, we had another baby on
the way. I had achieved more than I was expecting, but had not

yet gained a research degree (a research degree is one where a significant element of the degree involves research that was novel and original). Without this, there was no chance of becoming a clinical academic (a doctor who does both research and clinical medicine). And in the absence of a research degree the window of opportunity for this career path was closing fast.

I had decided to specialise in photodermatology (skin conditions characterised by sensitivity to sunlight), a sub-speciality of dermatology which was completely absent from this part of the UK. It appealed to me because it was possible to objectively measure and assess the disease using sophisticated optical phototesting equipment. I knew it to be a field of dermatology characterised by great suffering and disability for affected patients. This was a field of medicine where my efforts could make a difference to patient care. I was also attracted to photodermatology by the potential for clinical research. The best clinical research, I had discovered, involved looking at the condition from different but complementary perspectives: the patient (in other words, how the disease has an impact on the patient and their quality of life); the dermatologist (in other words, the clinical features observed and recorded in the skin by the clinician); and objective laboratory-based investigation. If all three were done to a high standard, it was possible to generate high quality research which was able to advance our understanding of these diseases. With improved understanding came the potential for developing new treatments, which in turn could move things forward to improve patient care.

In 1994, Professor Ronnie Marks helped me to set up a new clinic at the University Hospital of Wales in Cardiff. I was a consultant dermatologist in Newport, but did one day per week in Cardiff running this new photodermatology clinic. We took referrals from consultant dermatologists across South Wales, the Midlands, Bristol and the south-west of England, a huge catchment population for this new clinic dedicated to patients with sensitivity to sunlight. In one of my first clinics, a boy aged six attended with his parents. The room for the clinic was cramped: three medical staff, and Howard and his parents. Howard had profound learning difficulties and was also physically disabled. He was tiny for his age, sitting in a giant pushchair, being unable to walk. Although unable to talk, Howard smiled a lot and made affectionate babyish sounds by way of communication. His parents were both loving and attentive, completely relaxed with his care, attending to his needs. It was apparent that they had limited funds, and were coping as best they could with the challenges of caring for their son. They knew all about the health consequences of this metabolic condition.

'When did you first become aware that Howard was sensitive to sunlight?' I began with.

'As soon as we took him outside as a baby. It was March, the first hint of spring. Howard was nearly six months old. I took him outside in my arms, wrapped up because it was still a bit chilly. Only his face and hands were showing.'

'And what happened?'

'Howard started crying. He was such a contented and placid baby; this was unusual. I sniffed his bum, thinking he might have pooed himself, but all was well. I took him back inside to try to calm him down. When I took off his clothes, I noticed his face and hands were bright red, like sunburn.'

Howard had a brother and two sisters, none of whom were affected by photosensitivity. They showed me photographs (this was pre-mobile phones), which included a family shot on the beach. In the middle of the group picture was someone small, wearing a home-made one-piece suit, covering all of the skin, including the face, with small holes for the eyes and mouth: it was Howard, enjoying a day on the beach with his family.

After this consultation I did some background reading. I also spoke to other colleagues around the UK who specialised in photodermatology. No one knew anything about this condition, and there was nothing about it in the dermatology literature. It was apparent that this was a new, previously unrecognised photosensitivity condition. I then heard about a trainee geneticist in Newcastle, Anna, who was doing research into this metabolic condition. Two thirds of the twenty-five children she had seen in the UK with this condition shared this story of sun sensitivity. It turned out that these kids also had multiple health issues: feeding difficulties; digestive difficulties; failure to grow; profound physical problems; behavioural problems; speech and language difficulties. According to Anna, sensitivity to sunlight came very low on the hierarchy of problems that the parents were faced with. Furthermore, covering the skin with clothing or sunscreen seemed to solve the problem for most of these kids. Howard was the exception, as his parents were determined that he should join his siblings for trips to the beach. In other words, it was the context of the sun sensitivity that was making Howard's parents seek help, which led to them attending my new skin photosensitivity clinic in Cardiff.

We arranged for Howard to attend for special phototesting, to determine the nature of the photosensitivity. We also observed the skin reaction first hand, observing what happened to a small area of exposed skin following a few minutes of sun exposure. We carried out some blood tests to exclude other forms of photosensitivity, and wrote up the case for publication as a case report in the *British Journal of Dermatology*. We included photos of the skin reactions to sunlight, and reported the specialised photosensitivity tests carried out. This would be a first report of a new photosensitivity disorder. Howard's parents had consented to their son's case being published in a medical journal.

I had also decided to carry out a UK-wide study, as I was convinced that it was more than coincidence and actually represented a new and hitherto unreported form of photosensitivity. Howard's case had led to the identification of an important feature of this new photosensitivity condition: it was mediated by ultraviolet A radiation (UVA). UVA is biologically much less potent than ultraviolet B radiation, which is primarily responsible for sunburn reactions in the skin. This was relevant to Howard, as conventional sunscreens at that time were mainly formulated to protect against UVB. He required a sunscreen which protected against UVA as well as UVB, to prevent sunburn when on the beach at Southerndown, Ogmore-by-Sea or Barry Island with his siblings. I was now able to explain this to Howard's parents, and prescribe a suitable sunscreen. I also recommended that the family car to be fitted with special clear window film to block UVA, to make it safer for Howard. It was great to know that these small practical measures would help to prevent future painful sunburn reactions.

This discovery enabled me to carry out a systematic study on this new inherited photosensitivity syndrome; it would be ideal for a medical doctorate. Fortunately, the NHS was supportive. The medical director of my trust granted me one day per week for my medical doctorate studies. I found myself a research supervisor at King's College, London and wrote a study proposal. I then registered for a medical doctorate degree with the University of London. Within two years I had completed the project, written it up and submitted my thesis. I also gained a number of publications along the way, which helped to establish me within the UK academic community of photodermatology. I successfully defended my thesis and the medical doctorate was awarded by London University.

With the medical doctorate secured, I now needed to develop my own strategy for research. This time I was able to take over unused offices at St Woolos Hospital in Newport and set up a small academic dermatology unit. This was the base from which to coordinate courses and commercial clinical trials to generate an income stream to support our research; before long we had an active unit run by a small team of administration staff.

I focused on one postgraduate research student at a time; over the next fifteen years I supervised five junior dermatologists in medical doctorate projects. Two of these five MDs were on porphyrias, the disorder I went to South Africa to study in 2005. One particularly interesting condition called erythropoietic protoporphyria, or EPP for short, is a hard condition to diagnose as there is often nothing to see. Patients develop intense pain in their skin within a few minutes of being in bright sunshine. Most patients experienced the onset of these symptoms in early childhood, often before they could properly articulate what they were feeling. As there was nothing to see, their parents tended not to be taken too seriously when they sought advice from their GP a few days after an episode of skin pain. The pain was so severe that these children rapidly sought the shade or went indoors again. If they were quick enough, the pain subsided within minutes, and all was well. However, these symptoms impacted significantly on the child's quality of life, preventing participation in outdoor pursuits.

Jess came from Yorkshire. She enjoyed telling the story of her mother taking her as a young girl to see the local GP in a village not far from Leeds.

'She took me t' see the GP after I had suffered a really painful episode of sun-induced skin pain on't previous weekend. I was 'bout eight years old. The GP said that all was well, and there was nothing to worry about, and in future mi mam should apply more sunscreen, and no I didn't need to see a specialist at Jimmies [St James's Hospital in Leeds]. Mi mam hit the roof. She started shouting at the GP and told him he didn't know nothin, and could she see a better GP, and he must think she was soft-tween ears for thinking her kids were unwell when there was nowt wrong with'm. Corse she knew when there was something wrong! How dare he doubt a mother's word about her bearns!'

The GP changed his tune. Both Jess and her brother (who had similar but milder symptoms) were referred to the local dermatology service, where the diagnosis of EPP was eventually established in both children by characteristic changes in a blood test.

The University Hospital of Wales in Cardiff was already long-established as a pre-eminent centre for porphyria diagnosis and research on account of the professor of biochemistry, who also happened to be our next-door neighbour. When he retired, he was replaced by Mike, a young biochemistry consultant. Mike and I set up a cutaneous porphyria clinic and forged a research partnership: Mike had access to the labs and had biochemical expertise; I had access to the patients and clinical expertise. Our first big project was a UK-wide study on EPP, set up as an MD project for Dr Alex Holme, a Scottish dermatologist who was training in Cardiff.

Two years later we published a large cross-sectional study of EPP in the UK with over 200 patients recruited. This was a key paper for patients with EPP and was followed by many similar papers from around the globe. The combination of carefully recorded clinical features, high quality biochemistry and genetics studies, and the use of a validated quality of life questionnaire in all patients created three different perspectives of the same disorder. It was a potent combination; one we were to repeat in our next big porphyria research study. Alex Holme was first author on a number of studies that were generated by this MD project. He passed his MD with style. An unexpected outcome of this research was the identification of a small group of patients with features that were slightly at odds with the other patients. It transpired that we had inadvertently identified a new and hitherto unrecognised form of porphyria. We collaborated with colleagues in South Africa and France, as they too had small numbers of similar cases. Together we had enough cases to prove the point. The science was strong, and the paper was published in a top American genetics journal.

The second porphyria medical doctorate project we set up was for Dr Ru Katugampola. Ru had confirmed herself to be a hard-working, bright doctor, and was keen to do a research degree before she completed her training in dermatology and became a consultant. There was growing research interest in the most severe and mutilating form of porphyria, congenital erythropoietic porphyria, or 'CEP' for short. As a result of the structure of the NHS and the collaborative nature of the biochemical labs, it was possible to set up a UK study on this very rare condition. We identified seventeen cases across the UK, but really needed a few more. We again collaborated with porphyria experts (and friends) based in France and in Switzerland. With the additional cases, we had twenty-six patients. All patients were visited by Ru, who systematically gathered together the data, photographs and testing that we were seeking. It was the largest and most detailed study of this rare condition that had ever been performed. Again, we used the tried and tested technique of studying the condition from three complementary perspectives: the patient's own, by quality of life studies; the dermatologist's, through carefully standardised photography of skin lesions and identification of the features; and the laboratory studies, with high quality biochemistry and genetics studies. The overall aim of the study was to come up with a way to help parents of children affected by CEP when faced with the question of a potentially curative bone marrow transplant, the issue being that such a procedure was potentially life-threatening and was not always a success.

Ru Katugampola passed her MD with great aplomb, impressing the examiners in the process. Another successful MD, a string of important research findings which were published in top journals, and important research advances in this challenging condition.

By this stage my research interests were broadening. In 1999 I was appointed by the health board as associate medical director for research and development. I was always on the lookout for research methods or ideas that could be applied to improving NHS clinical services. An area that I had become aware of was mathematical modelling. I knew about using this approach as a research tool, but was drawn to mathematical modelling and computer simulation as a way to bring new thinking and a different approach to long-standing issues that affected the NHS. The issues were too complex for standard problem-solving, being multi-layered, with complex interrelationships. Interventions aimed at solving long-standing issues often failed due to a lack of understanding of the whole system dynamics. It was often possible to fix one part of the system, only to discover the knock-on effect to another part of the system. We needed something that could allow us to better understand this complexity, in order to make better and smarter interventions.

•   •   •

A SIX-YEAR-OLD CHILD
WITH SENSITIVITY TO VISIBLE LIGHT

Riinu is just six years old. Her skin is still almost blemish-free, just a few small scabs and scars on the back of her hands, and partial separation of the end of a fingernail. Mum and dad are intelligent and attentive; both have well-paid jobs. They are also first cousins; they carried the same mutated gene, harmless in isolation, but harmful if joined in their offspring by a mutation in the same gene inherited from the other parent. This is what had happened in Riinu. They were in the porphyria clinic to better understand the treatment options for Riinu. Riinu is suffering from congenital porphyria, a metabolic disorder with the potential to cause severe scarring and mutilation of sun-exposed skin. Riinu is exquisitely sensitive to visible light. For her skin to remain undamaged, when outside, she would need to cover up with clothing, gloves and a mask to block out all light, for the rest of her life. 'We can't do that to her,' they tell me. 'Kids need to go outside and play.' 'Of course they do,' I agree. We go over it carefully, not rushing the discussion. The only way that Riinu can have a normal life is to have a bone marrow transplant. But this is risky, with failure of the procedure and even death as possible outcomes. How to decide? It is an agonising and impossible choice. We are trying to aid the decision-making process, to help mum and dad to think it through, not to make decisions for them. 'There is also the prospect of future gene therapy,' we tell them; not as fanciful as it sounded. We know the French porphyria group are close to achieving this.

CHAPTER 18

ACADEMIC PARTNERSHIPS

2011–2015

The idea was to create computer-based models to replicate the complexity and dynamic nature of healthcare; a model to determine how many ambulances are required and where they should be optimally positioned in the catchment area to ensure that response times for urgent calls that were fast enough, for example. Professor Paul Harper's expertise was operational research using mathematical modelling in healthcare. Paul wondered if I would like to create a project and host a mathematics master's degree student? Three months later, Kayne joined us at St Woolos Hospital in Newport for a four-month stint. His task was to create a model, using a technique called 'discrete event simulation', to assist the dermatology team in planning services for patients with psoriasis. The model was computer-based, looking like a giant two-dimensional schematic diagram: new patients entered at one end of the figure, and treated patients exited elsewhere. Between these two points, patients flowed along pathways through different treatment options represented by boxes. It reminded me of the maps used in the Battle of Britain control room, with small painted model planes being moved around on the map by women in uniform with long wooden shoving sticks. This part of our service was expensive and complicated, with multiple treatment options available. Our theory was that more patients would opt for ultraviolet light therapy if it was available at more locations, creating better patient access. But new ultraviolet light therapy treatment units were costly to set up and staff, so where would the money come from?

The model had to be able to cope with this complexity, whilst also showing the ebb and flow of patients as they went through the system. If sufficiently realistic and valid this model could help the clinical team of doctors and nurses to conceptualise our services being delivered in a different way. With cost a key issue, we needed a dynamic model to better understand the wider provision of a cheap treatment (ultraviolet light therapy), perhaps funded by the resulting decrease in demand for the more expensive treatments (biological and immune-suppressant tablet therapies for psoriasis and inpatient care). We were trying to understand patient flow through the system, whilst also addressing the need to offer treatments that fitted with patient preferences within a tight budget. The ambition was to significantly change the system without spending more money.

Kayne showed us how the model worked on a large computer screen; he then ran dummy scenarios to test it. The whole team accepted that the model was valid, and that the results it obtained in these test runs were believable. We agreed that the model could therefore be used for service-planning purposes. The model showed us that investment in phototherapy services would indeed save money by reducing patient flow towards expensive and potentially more risky treatments; this was what we had predicted. The paper was accepted for oral presentation at the British Association of Dermatologists' annual meeting; it was well received. Soon after, it was accepted for publication, remaining one of a small number of publications to have researched patient flow in psoriasis.

The following year we came up with another mathematical modelling project using a technique linking the population in three large health boards across Wales to local towns and cities where phototherapy services could be offered, and calculating the distance each patient would need to travel for this treatment. Harriet, the master's degree student, developed a model that could be used for planning phototherapy services to ensure the optimum blend between fixed phototherapy hubs (where patients travel to and from the phototherapy unit at a hospital to have their treatment administered by a nurse) and home units (where the patient treats themselves at home using a special home UV treatment unit). This was a creative project which was unimaginable from standard NHS planners. It led to a Welsh Government grant application to set up new, more accessible phototherapy services in three health boards.

Professor Paul Harper had four final-year PhD students whose research projects utilised mathematical modelling in healthcare. In the School of Mathematics, they were fondly referred to as 'the Fab Four'. Paul was wondering if my health board might like to employ them? He was asking me in my capacity as director of research and development for the health board; this was within my brief, but not within my ability to gift. I liked the idea and approached Andrew Goodall, the chief executive of the health board. I knew that Andrew was keen on research. He also liked the idea, and offered a one-hour slot for Paul and his team to pitch to the executive board. If the health board executives supported it, he told me, so would he.

It was all set up a few weeks later in the boardroom at Mamhilad Park, Pontypool. Professor Paul Harper brought a team of three: he headed the presentation, supported by two leading academics in his department, Janet Williams and Vincent Knight. Each spoke about a different aspect of mathematical modelling in healthcare.

Paul began by showing a cartoon to introduce queuing theory, with someone switching from one queue to another in their attempt to get to the front; the audience laughed. They all knew about NHS waiting lists and queuing. Paul went on to explain some simple concepts in mathematical modelling in healthcare, establishing his team's credentials. He then illustrated the complexity of patient flow with a whole-system mathematical model of an ear, nose and throat clinic. This was based on a real NHS clinic using the techniques of discrete event simulation combined with optimisation. Once again, Paul had the audience's attention; I could see them leaning forward in their chairs, listening intently to what he was saying. Paul talked them through the model, which was illustrated on the screen by a large simplified cartoon of the clinic, with Lowry-like stick people representing patients and staff. He explained that the mathematical algorithms behind the model were hidden from view. The model on the screen showed a schematic diagram of a virtual clinic. Having explained the elements of the clinic, he then showed it in action, with patients arriving at 9 a.m. and the clinic finishing at 12:30 p.m. He was able to show patient flow through the clinic, with three and a half hours compressed into just sixty seconds. It was mesmerising seeing the queues building up and then dissolving at the end of the clinic. He then changed the model to show the effect of adding or removing elements on overall patient flow and efficiency of the clinic. How would an extra audiologist affect patient flow in this clinic? How about one more consultant? I watched the audience as it dawned on them that here was a smarter way of doing heath care than they were used to. One by one, the expressions on their faces changed from polite but indifferent, to interested and fully engaged.

Next up was Janet Williams, a senior mathematician. She talked about the complexity of planning staffing levels for different parts of the hospital. Too many on call means staff are sitting around with nothing to do and high costs; too few staff mean they are overly busy, and health care may be compromised, although costs are lower. There was also staff sickness to consider, and the high cost of agency staff and locums to plug unexpected gaps in the service. Add into this the variable levels of demand according to days of the week or the weather and it is easy to see that planning staffing rosters was a thankless task with a high risk of error. Janet then shared a research project which sought to anticipate the ebb and flow of demand according to season, day of the week, and the weather. It was clever stuff, linked to data from the Met Office, and historical patterns of demand for the local population. Instead of using guesswork, and hoping for the best, Janet showed a system that could predict spikes in demand before they happened. Armed with this insight, it was then possible to organise the staff roster to match the anticipated demand. The director of nursing and the director of human resources could not contain themselves: both asked questions to clarify how this system worked. There was a growing sense of excitement around the table.

Vincent Knight, the youngest of the three mathematicians, talked about research on optimising patient flow through an accident and emergency department, the front door to the hospital. This was high-stakes healthcare; if you get it wrong, the ambulances start stacking up outside A&E and the hospital ends up on the local TV news that night. Again, it was a complex issue which resonated with the audience; there were multiple variables to consider. This was part of the problem; it was too complex to be solved by standard thought processes and systems. There were just too many variables to take into account: staffing levels; staffing skill mix; number of bays to see patients; access to imaging services; portering services; the weather; local sporting events; the possibility of a major incident. This was a research project which had taken place just a few miles down the road at the University Hospital of Wales. A new system for Accident and Emergency had been created on the back of this research, with patient flow and use of A&E resources optimised.

By the time the presentation reached the stage of proposing collaboration between the university and the health board, the health board's executive officers appeared to be convinced of the relevance of this novel approach to problem-solving in the complex arena of NHS healthcare. However, the CEO, Andrew

Goodall, had missed the presentations as he was dealing with an unscheduled emergency; he had spent the whole meeting in his office taking a phone call from the Welsh Minister for Health. The next step, if there was to be one, would be his call. He scheduled another meeting a few days later; this time it would be just the four of us, Andrew, Paul, Sue Bale (deputy director of research and development) and me.

I was optimistic. I had established a bond with Andrew based on our discussions about research and innovation. He had shared his research experiences with Sue Bale and me and had talked with passion about his PhD, which had compared the French health service with the UK's NHS. At the time of his research, the UK and France's health care systems had much in common. (This has now changed following years of lower funding for the NHS compared to France's much better funded service.) Andrew was one of the first speakers at a lunchtime seminar series Sue and I set up to broaden staff's research horizons within the health board.

It didn't take long before Andrew let us know that the Executive Officers had agreed to support his proposal to offer four PhD students two-year contracts with the health board when they graduated later this year. In other words, he had accepted the plan for the health board to recruit four experts on mathematical modelling in healthcare. Although this was what we were hoping for, it still surprised us when it happened.

A few months later, the Fab Four joined Aneurin Bevan University Health Board as employees in the newly created Mathematical Modelling Unit: Dr Julie Vile, Dr Penny Holborn, Dr Izabela Spernaes (née Komenda) and Dr Tracey

England. Professor Sue Bale and I worked hard to ensure they fitted in, with an induction programme that took account of their lack of experience of working in the NHS. We were anxious that they might find the transition from university to NHS difficult, and were keen to make their recruitment a success. We need not have worried; Julie, Penny, Iza and Tracey all had exceptional interpersonal skills and engaging, outgoing personalities. They soon fitted in; word was out that their approach to problem-solving informed by data could help to tackle the toughest of healthcare problems. Nevertheless, there was still a sense that a Mathematical Modelling Unit staffed by four mathematicians was an odd thing to have within the health board. What followed was an example of one thing logically leading to the next; a positive domino effect.

The Aneurin Bevan Health Board had recently changed medical directors: out went Dr Stephen Hunter, the supremely successful visionary, strategist and long-term planner, retiring after more than ten years in the role; in came Dr Grant Robinson, a consultant haematologist with a passion for health service improvement, as pioneered and promoted by Professor Don Berwick and others. Within a few months, Grant had created a health service improvement unit, with the snappy title of ABCi (Aneurin Bevan Continuous Improvement). This unit pulled together health board staff with skills, knowledge and experience that were essential if service improvement was to succeed. At the core of this unit were the four mathematical modellers; an ideal arrangement, with the intellectual core powering the activity of the unit. The presence of our mathematical modellers no longer looked like something interesting and unexpected that had washed up on the beach; it all fitted together perfectly, creating a coherent whole.

Ten years on, I would go back and ask Paul Harper if the Fab Four had lived up to his hopes to embed operational research within the NHS, knowing that universities must use partnerships outside academia to embed new knowledge and new ways of working.

In answer to my question, Paul told me that his university academic unit were still collaborating with ABCi. Since the initial Fab Four, various researchers had come and gone; throughout this decade they had maintained an effective and highly productive team. Those that left went on to other key posts and had clearly benefitted from their experience. One was employed directly by ABCi. Another joined Paul's team at the university and was later directly employed by Aneurin Bevan University Health Board. A third individual joined and later went on to gain a permanent university lectureship. One of the original Fab Four worked for six years with ABCi before moving to a staff post with Cancer Research UK. The biggest development during this period was that Aneurin Bevan University Health Board and Cardiff University match-funded a permanent lectureship, the Aneurin Bevan Lecturer in Operational Research, a post held by the appointee since January 2016. This person works between both organisations and turned out to be an amazing appointment; with boundless energy and ideas, he quickly worked his way to become a professor. Paul concluded by saying that this collaboration between university and the NHS had generated lots of PhD-funded projects and MSc projects over the years and had led to the setting up of the Analytics and Modelling Academy, to train non-mathematician staff in data management and data analysis. In other words, a ripple effect, with excellence spreading across the health board. This collaboration was acknowledged by the award of a prestigious annual award in 2021 by the UK Operational Research Society. The award cited 150 completed projects over eight years, and evidenced cost savings for the NHS of at least £12.1 million. Two projects stood out in their list of successes: informing the design of a new hospital leading to ongoing savings of £900,000 per year compared to the original design through more efficient scheduling of operating theatres; designing service delivery support for mental health outreach teams leading to a reduction in avoidable hospital admissions of nearly 80%, and a reduction in time taken off work by patients of 65% due to severe mental health episodes. Importantly, all of this work resulted in a good amount of societal impact that the team had captured. This was not a zero-sum game; it was mutually beneficial to both partners, the NHS and the university, who were doing more together than either could do on their own.

I realised then that Paul had highlighted an important point. One way to assess the impact of our efforts in academia is by considering their impact on society. For a doctor, this all starts with patient care. What impact were we making on the local population with the service that we were running, and how best to assess this? It dawned on me that we needed to be able to see our clinical service through a different lens: the lens of the patient in the community. But how?

*　　*　　*

FEMALE, AGE TWENTY-SIX,
UNSIGHTLY MOLE LEFT CHEEK

Clare is twenty-six, with a prominent and unsightly brown mole on her left cheek. I am surprised she has lived with it for so long. I explain what I will do. 'It's called a shave excision. I will numb the skin with an injection. After that, you won't feel anything. Then I will use a special blade to slice the mole off, flush to the skin. This will leave the raw base of the mole, which will be bleeding from a few tiny blood vessels called capillaries. I will seal these capillaries with liquid aluminium chloride applied via a sterile cotton bud. It takes about two minutes to stop bleeding. Then, a tiny dressing, and we are done.'

'No stitches?'

'No stitches.'

'And the final cosmetic result?'

'…is usually excellent.'

'Let's do it!'

CHAPTER 19

PATIENT PARTNERSHIPS

2005-2015

I began now to see how the cases presented by patients could feed into clinical research. One was not possible without the other. Thanks to our patients, the research moved from the theoretical and abstract, into making a difference to real lives. Patients enjoyed being listened to and taken seriously by researchers. Furthermore, if they were involved in the early planning stages, projects were improved. This was the difference between tokenism, where the aim is to tick a box, and empowerment, where the aim is to unleash and then capture patient perspectives in our research activities.

The rules governing clinical research meant that projects could not proceed without patient engagement. It was the late 1990s. A prominent and articulate patient advocate was Peter Lapsley, the CEO of the National Eczema Society, a skin charity based in London. Academic Dermatology, our research and teaching unit in Newport, had recently been established in an old part of the hospital that had previously been the local workhouse. I met him to discuss how best to use patient stories to advance our agendas: in Peter's case to raise awareness about the impact of skin disease on patient's quality of life; in my case to use patient stories as a tool for research and education.

Peter had inspired me to create an environment in my clinical and academic practice where patient stories could be captured. A few weeks later, I invited Anthony Meyer to a teaching session for local GPs in Newport. Tony was in his late thirties, a life-long sufferer from eczema. I knew him well and was confident that he would communicate his story effectively. The audience of about forty-five GPs were assembled for an after-work meeting in the Friars Postgraduate Medical Centre in Newport. Tony worked in human resources for a multinational company; he was used to public speaking, but had never previously talked about his skin disease. We agreed that he would tell his life story through his experiences of living with eczema, with photographs to bring it to life. After a brief introduction, I sat down to watch and listen. This was the first time I had trusted a patient to take the lead role in a teaching session; I was excited to see how he would be received.

As his story unfolded, a hush descended on the room. Tony told us about his childhood, and the teasing at school. His nature was positive and outgoing. He then explained the darker side of life with eczema. Sleep deprivation and severe itch had impacted negatively on his quality of life, particularly in his teens. 'It affected everything!' he told the audience, relationships in particular. He told us about meeting his wife in his mid-twenties, and how life changed for the better once he had his own loving and supportive family. He concluded by telling us about his career, and how his eczema had affected his work. He finished on an upbeat note, telling us how recent treatment with a drug called azathioprine had been effective at suppressing his eczema. When he finished, he was met by a round of applause. The feedback from the GPs was some of the most positive I have seen for a teaching event.

A few weeks later, I saw Tony in the clinic for a review appointment. He was clearly pleased that his talk had gone well. I asked if he would be willing to help out with a clinical guideline I was co-authoring on azathioprine prescribing in dermatology? We needed a patient on our authorship team, to provide the patient perspective. He accepted, and contributed to the process as an active team member, acknowledged in print when it was published in the *BJD*.

My networking meeting with Peter Lapsley a few months earlier had already influenced me to work in a different way. This felt like the right thing to do, and improved my teaching and academic writing activities.

At a team meeting a few months later in Academic Dermatology, we discussed how to increase patient engagement. Having expert patients as part of the faculty had been a great success, bringing a new dimension to our teaching. The feedback from delegates had been positive, the expert patients scoring as highly as the clinicians on our team. But something was missing.

'Why don't you have patients on your team for your NHS clinical service?' said Jane.

Brilliant.

The way forward was to create a local patient advocacy group for dermatology. I studied similar groups around the UK, but none were doing what I was seeking. For this to work, the group needed to develop its own way of working and must be independent. The clinicians on our team started collecting names of patients who might be suitable. It was agreed that thirty or more would be needed, anticipating a high dropout rate. The group would need some financial support to get going, and professional help to develop a simple constitution. It then became apparent that a few meetings would be necessary before things were formalised, so that the group understood what was being asked of them.

I invited the dermatology charity Skin Care Cymru to help with the meeting, the only skin charity in Wales. They were financially independent of the bigger skin charities, but matched the ambition of English and Scottish charities set up at the same time under the 'Skin Care Campaign' banner. By creating a local dermatology patient group in Gwent, we would extend the reach and influence of Skin Care Cymru. Three early evening meetings were arranged, at four-weekly intervals. Sixteen patients attended the first meeting, some with spouses and partners. The next two meetings were also well attended, and a shared agenda gradually emerged. The group named itself the Gwent Dermatology Patient Panel (GDPP). Once set up, I left them to their own devices, pledging my support if needed. Softly spoken Pam Fudge was elected to the role of chairperson. She proved to be an effective and tenacious leader, and was still there ten years later.

My involvement with this group opened my eyes to dermatology clinical services as seen from the perspective of patients.

The GDPP was successful at a number of levels. They were able to provide better information to local patients about dermatology services. They were available to listen to patients' views on local healthcare services. Through work with the local clinical lead for NHS dermatology they were able to improve patient access to services, such as phototherapy. Furthermore, the GDPP was increasingly used as a resource by our local NHS dermatology team to help improve the quality of services. They acted as a mirror for us as local clinicians as we sought to improve the monitoring of our clinical services. The group also helped Academic Dermatology to increase recruitment into clinical trials and other research. Importantly, this group was able to make the local NHS more accountable to the local community and to increase transparency on strategic matters. The Aneurin Bevan University Health Board chief executive, Andrew Goodall, was accountable for implementing the patient engagement agenda across the whole of the NHS in Gwent. Dermatology was now a discipline where he could point to a clinical service and confirm that this was happening.

• • •

We now needed our own local dermatology patient panel in North Wales. We set things in motion, the team collecting names of patients who had shown interest in this idea. In June of 2015 the health board had been placed in 'special measures', a form of probation with Welsh Government, in response to poor performance, particularly in mental health services. One issue was that the organisation was poor at listening and responding to local patients and the public. I was surprised to discover that this would be the first patient advocacy group to be set up in this health board; it was no wonder the organisation was in special measures, with a reputation for not listening.

*   *   *

I was fortunate to witness patient engagement at a national level through my involvement with the National Institute for Health and Care Excellence (NICE). I represented dermatology specialists on three NICE committee meetings to consider approval for new, high-cost drugs to treat psoriasis (these meetings were called 'single technology appraisals'). It was interesting to witness this process as a participant, and to note that equal weight was given to the expert and patient voice; there were two subject experts on the committee, and two patient representatives. The rest of the committee were standing members, representing national professional bodies (nursing, medicine, pharmacology, the law, ethics and others), and numerous health economists. The patient representatives, both of whom I knew, were given the same time to speak and were treated in the same way as I was. This was patient and public involvement in action; it looked and sounded good. No wonder NICE has become such a key element of the NHS. I could see that NICE was a forum for all relevant groups including patients, where evidence-based medicine was reconciled with health economics.

One of the principal aims of NICE is to speed the uptake of healthcare interventions that are effective and represent value for money. NICE also aims to encourage more equitable access to healthcare, and to nurture and support the creation and dissemination of new, innovative technologies. All three of the single technology appraisals I attended as a subject expert were approved by NICE. All three of these drugs are still used; many of my patients are still on them. Despite being expensive, all three of these treatments are safe and effective, each with the potential to transform patient's lives. It is easy to take such progress for granted.

I still recall the days before these drugs, when some patients with bad skin disease were admitted to the dermatology ward to be treated as inpatients, sometimes for months at a time. It is hard to believe this really happened, but it did. Some of these patients volunteered to participate in clinical trials to assess the novel biological therapies. These were multi-centre, randomised controlled clinical trials, as advocated by Archie Cochrane. These UK trials often included patients from Academic Dermatology in Newport. I reflected that the element that made NICE so influential as a positive force in healthcare was the recognition of the value of patient and carer engagement in all stages of its activity.

Patient empowerment was an unexpected outcome for one clinical trial we did in 2009. This was a complex trial which involved time-consuming baseline light tests on patients, followed by administering a drug as a subcutaneous implant. The skin disease we were assessing was erythropoietic protoporphyria (EPP for short), a rare but disabling skin condition characterised by intense skin pain triggered by short exposure to sunlight. Our team had become experts on this condition as a result of our large UK study. We were one of only two UK centres chosen for this international study, and had been responsible for developing the light testing protocol to be used. Patients had travelled great distances to participate. Despite having a team of five staff, we soon became bogged down; everything took longer than we had anticipated. The patients were all together in a large waiting room, and gradually loosened up and started chatting to each other, recognising there was not much that they could do to speed things along. For most, it was the first time they had met someone else with the same condition. The mood changed from impatience to friendliness to bonhomie and then to something approaching elation. By the end of the day, the eight patients knew each well enough to agree to keep in touch after the study was completed and to set up a patient support group for their condition. This group rapidly became international, with nearly 200 patient members from all over the world. George, their chairperson and one of my patients, became a highly effective patient advocate. He spoke as a patient advocate at an international porphyria conference I helped to organise in Cardiff in 2012.

This group of patients had previously felt isolated, misunderstood, marginalised and ignored by healthcare services. The clinical trial was a success and was published in the *New England Journal of Medicine*, a prestigious medical journal. On this occasion, patient empowerment was a consequence of the research, as well as having been used as a building block to set up this project.

The *British Journal of Dermatology (BJD)* is a monthly peer-reviewed medical journal that covers the field of dermatology. On becoming editor, I was delighted to be able to put my beliefs about patient empowerment into journalistic and peer reviewed practice. One Saturday morning in 2014 I was sitting in the kitchen reading the patient story section in the *BMJ*. The author was a patient with severe skin disease, the text an insightful communication about a badly disrupted life. It was moving, quite unlike anything that was published in the *BJD* or any other dermatology journal. I read it carefully a second time, searching for more detail, and spotted a name I knew: Section Editor, Peter Lapsley. We had last been in touch ten years earlier, but the following Monday, I emailed him, congratulating him on his role and saying how much I had enjoyed this week's article. Could we meet up?

Peter Lapsley's role as patient editor of the *BMJ*, a section he had started in 2004, had been the most fulfilling job of his whole career. On an emotional level, he connected me to something important which I was unable to resist. In the coming years, patient engagement would become part of the mantra for the *BJD*.

The Cochrane Library practice of including a plain language summary at the start of most of their systematic reviews had the potential to open up the research findings to the public and patients. This resonated with me, as well as connecting two of my healthcare heroes, Archie Cochrane and William Osler. Osler, a Canadian, became famous as a leading doctor and prolific medical author in the late nineteenth and early twentieth centuries. It was Osler who had urged doctors to use plain language to explain complex topics: 'And from the standpoint of medicine as an art for the prevention and cure of disease, the man who translates the hieroglyphics of science into the plain language of healing is certainly the most useful.' The great success of Cochrane's book *Effectiveness and*

Efficiency was partly explained by its accessibility, readability and simplicity.

We followed this example and introduced plain language summaries to the *BJD* with the intention of helping patients to understand and access the original articles we published. Feedback from patients and patient groups concerning plain language summaries was universally positive. Could we do more, I was often asked, to connect and represent patients to research papers published in the *BJD*? One of my final editorials for the *BJD* concerned patient engagement, and the journal's strategy to make this a reality. Within twelve months of demitting as editor in 2019, two patients had been appointed as patient editors, their names on the journal masthead as members of the distinguished editorial team, an appointment they announced themselves with an editorial. Two years after leaving the journal, I was approached by a group of international scholars and invited to join an initiative to create a best practice guideline for authors on how to create plain language summaries for original research articles; I was the only clinician on the author group. At present very few academic publications include plain language summaries, perhaps fewer than 1 per cent. Thus, The Cochrane Library and the *BJD* are leading by example. This new guideline has the potential to help to transform and open up academic publishing to the public and to patients.

· · ·

SEVENTY-SIX-YEAR-OLD WIDOW
WITH AN ODD-LOOKING MOLE

She is in her mid-seventies, and recently bereaved. She and her husband had lived in Burgundy for twenty years, until he developed dementia. They came back to the UK two years ago, to be nearer to their son. She clearly likes navy blue: navy blue shoes, navy blue tights, navy blue skirt, navy blue blouse and a smart navy blue jacket, topped off with a navy blue headscarf. The mole on her arm had been there for five years and was getting bigger. I look at it carefully through the dermatoscope. 'Well?' she asks. 'What is it?'

'It looks like a blue naevus. Benign. Nothing to worry about, but best removed in view of the history of recent change.'

CHAPTER 20

SIR WILLIAM OSLER, MEDICAL HERO

2014

We were late. The coach driver had taken a wrong turn and we were stuck in Oxford's notorious traffic. I had organised this day out for my eight Bachelor of Science students, and three members of the Cardiff University medical education faculty. We were visiting 13 Norham Gardens, the former home of one of the most famous doctors in our profession, Sir William Osler. We were making our pilgrimage to learn more about him, and try to understand how he became so influential as a role model for doctors. Osler had loved this house, known fondly as the 'Open Arms' on account of the warm reception his many visitors received. The custodian of the house was Professor Terence Ryan, a retired professor of dermatology from Oxford who we' spotted outside the large Victorian Gothic house, his arms held aloft.

'Welcome,' he said.

In his early eighties, Terence still retained the sharp-witted aura of an academic at the top of his game. He had always been a great enthusiast, keen and willing to share his passions with others.

'Wasn't this rather a large house for Osler and his wife?' asked one of the students doubtfully, as he sized up what looked like a small hotel or a residential care home.

'Yes, indeed,' said Terence, 'but the Oslers had staff and many, many visitors.'

Terence then told us about the first-class medical library Osler created in his home, for which he needed plenty of space. He went on, 'The Oslers shared the house with a maid, a cook and a butler. Osler often joked that it was more like a hotel than a family home, and teased his wife Grace that she had missed her calling in not running a summer hotel. There were two guest rooms, Baltimore and Philadelphia, named after the two American cities where Osler's career had taken off. They hosted numerous guests at Norham Gardens including the American Ambassador to Great Britain, and the authors Mark Twain and Rudyard Kipling. Osler had known Mark Twain since 1881 when he had organised a dinner for the famous author in Montreal. However, the visit to Norham Gardens for luncheon was not a success; Twain rudely snubbed one of Grace Osler's American guests. In contrast, Rudyard Kipling was a delightful house guest. Kipling showed an interest in Osler's medical library and even took the young Revere, Grace and William's son, for a walk. They became close enough for Osler to persuade Kipling to cut down his smoking.'

Osler was no ordinary doctor. The royalties from his book, *The Principles and Practice of Medicine*, an international bestseller and already on its sixth edition by the time he and Grace purchased this house in 1905, were considerable. He was much in demand in his private practice, being one of the best-known doctors in the world. He was also paid a generous salary from Oxford University for the post of Regius Professor, a position light on duties but heavy with prestige. When he and Grace moved to Oxford in 1905, they were comfortably well off; indeed, far richer than most UK doctors. Osler had no need to build a large clinical practice, and opted instead to see just five or six private patients per week. By this time in his life, he was winding down from clinical medicine, focusing more on the next edition of his textbook, invited lectureships, cataloguing and adding to his library and, of course, his academic writing and editing. He had become fascinated by the history of medicine.

With selected memorabilia, the house had been restored, decorated and furnished to resemble Osler's former home. It was fascinating to sit in his study, look at books and manuscripts, squint at photographs on the walls, and try to imagine life in this house more than 100 years earlier. We wandered through the rooms, soaking up the atmosphere and trying our best to conjure up a sense of life here with the Oslers. Next, we walked around the garden, which bordered University Parks, giving it the feel of a country house.

'We are now standing in the room that Osler used as his office,' said Terence as we moved back inside. 'He and Grace lived in this house together for fourteen years, until Osler died here, aged seventy, in 1919. For Oxford University, his recruitment from Johns Hopkins Hospital in Baltimore was a triumph.'

Osler had grown up in rural Ontario, Canada, and graduated in medicine from McGill University, Montreal. He was sponsored by his brother to travel to Europe for postgraduate medical training and networking in London, Berlin and Vienna, before returning to Canada as assistant professor at McGill. McGill had a tradition of bedside teaching and Osler rapidly became its leading exponent. He came into his own, becoming a prolific medical writer and developing a reputation for being observant, logical and well read.

He then moved to the USA, as chair of clinical medicine at the University of Pennsylvania in Philadelphia. Five years later he moved again, this time to the prestigious new Johns Hopkins Hospital in Baltimore as physician-in-chief and then professor of medicine at the new School of Medicine. At the same time, he published his textbook, *The Principles and Practice of Medicine*, an immediate hit, which secured Osler a significant and steady income for the rest of his life. His timing was good, as previous textbooks of medicine had become outdated, their famous authors too old to create new editions. A gap had appeared in the market, which Osler's textbook filled. Furthermore, it coincided with the general rise in the reputation and prestige of the practice of medicine in America. The market for a textbook of medicine written in English by a pre-eminent American was huge.

Alongside his formidable writing skills was his style of medicine, which proved quite different to what had come before. He was humanistic, his patient interactions characterised by compassion, kindness and respect. He was relentlessly positive and good humoured to fellow human beings, especially his patients. From this he created the persona of the selfless physician, willing to go to great efforts on behalf of his patients. In contrast, previous generations of doctors had often used their profession as a way to enrich themselves at the expense of their patients, and were typically aloof and remote, often speaking down to their patients. Osler integrated his bedside manner with his learning. He was happy to share his scientific and clinical knowledge with his patients. Out went quackery, in came the application of scientific and clinical knowledge derived from his deep understanding of medical science. Medicine had finally become a profession, with Osler as its leading exponent, and, in addition, a dedicated and inspiring educator, passionate about training medical students and young doctors. Johns Hopkins School of Medicine quickly acquired the reputation as the very best place in the USA to study medicine, with Osler as the figurehead. Thanks also to Osler's academic writing – he wrote many hundreds of papers as a generalist, which helped to underpin the academic rigour and reputation of his bestselling textbook – he was able to pass on his practice to every generation since.

'The best doctor, like the successful general, is the one who makes the fewest mistakes,' he was fond of saying.

Most of his books were bequeathed to McGill University in Osler's will. The collection was packed into eighty-six cases containing 8,000 books, and shipped to Montreal in the autumn of 1928. The Osler Library finally opened at McGill nearly ten years after Osler's death, in May 1929. The library catalogue ran to 786 pages. The small number of books now in the house were collected together by Osler scholars after the Osler Library had been shipped to Canada.

What would Osler have said to these eight medical students concerning general advice on the art of doctoring, I wondered, before recalling another well-known Osler quote.

'Mastery of self, conscientious devotion to duty, deep human interest in human beings. These best of all lessons you must learn now or never.'

• • •

MALE, TWENTY-FOUR, CHRONIC IMMUNOSPRESSION

Donald is in his mid-twenties, but has the aura of a child. He sustained brain damage during his first kidney transplant aged fourteen, which has left him disabled. He walks with a stiff gait, and his mental capacity is about that of a twelve-year-old. He loves football and is an avid fan of Swindon Town. The club have embraced him; he is part of their football family. He attends my clinic with skin problems resulting from long-term immunosuppression. The second kidney transplant was a success. Our consultations are always enjoyable. Donald is gleeful if Crystal Palace (my team) have lost, pretending to be sad for me, and insisting on talking about it. If Palace have won, he says nothing, waiting for me to mention it, and is quick to chide me for showing off. As for Swindon Town FC, if I asked, we could easily be there for another twenty minutes. During this banter, I treat his latest crop of warts with cryotherapy.

'See you in four months, or sooner if necessary,' I say.

'Good luck on Saturday!' he says. 'Maybe Palace will win this time?'

CHAPTER 21

DR EDWARD JENNER, MEDICAL HERO

2014

Our visit to another house of a famous doctor on that memorable student day trip from Cardiff University in 2014 was timely. Six years later, Jenner's name would be in the national news: it was at the Jenner Institute that Professor Sarah Gilbert developed the Oxford–AstraZeneca COVID-19 vaccine. Named after Dr Edward Jenner, the institute was formed to help develop vaccines and coordinate clinical trials for the treatment of malaria, tuberculosis, ebola and SARS-coronavirus, some of the most important ongoing threats to the health of humankind.

Jenner's home, a fine-looking country house, with two prominent chimney stacks, a large kitchen garden, outbuildings, a stable block and green houses, sits in the heart of rural Gloucestershire, close to the River Severn. Our visit included a lecture from a Jenner scholar, who explained to us how Jenner's prowess as a scientist was apparent early in his career. His publication in *Philosophical Transactions of the Royal Society* described the behaviour of the newly hatched cuckoo chick. It had previously been assumed that the adult cuckoo came back to dispose of the other chicks when the cuckoo chick hatched. Jenner demonstrated that it was the cuckoo chick itself who committed fratricide.

We also heard how Jenner's experience of getting his cuckoo paper published made it easier for him when the cowpox vaccination story was ready to be written up. Jenner had observed that milkmaids in his rural medical practice in Gloucestershire where exposed to cowpox by milking infected cows. He also observed that these same milkmaids seemed never to become infected by smallpox, a much more serious and often life-threatening disease. Like others before him, Jenner surmised that deliberately infecting humans with cowpox would protect them from contracting smallpox. Years before he became fixated by cowpox and smallpox, Jenner's earlier research and subsequent published report on cuckoo behaviour had been greeted with scepticism. His cuckoo paper was subsequently validated by the expert wildlife artist Jemima Blackburn and then by Charles Darwin; it was even included in revised versions of Darwin's *On the Origin of Species*. This experience of rejection and scepticism followed eventually by acceptance was crucial in preparing Jenner for the fight ahead to get his cowpox/smallpox vaccination story accepted.

Jenner had married well. His wealth was a key part of the story, as it allowed him to self-publish. His initial scientific paper on cowpox/smallpox, written in 1796, was deemed by experts at the Royal Society as inadequate to support his claims; he was advised to gather more evidence. As with Osler, Jenner recognised that writing up and publishing novel ideas was as important as having the ideas. It was only when his ideas were published that, for example, Jenner's concept of vaccination could be considered by the medical community; a form of early peer review. This in turn led to acceptance. Jenner's proposal about cowpox protecting against smallpox was confirmed to be true. A few others had the same idea as Jenner, in some instances many years earlier. But it was Jenner who systematically and scientifically recorded his observations, wrote them up and published.

Jenner's cowpox vaccination monograph was published at his own expense in June 1798, a time when the threat of smallpox to public health meant that 10 per cent of the population would die of the disease, more in urban areas. It was even worse in continental Europe. Voltaire, writing in France nearly thirty years earlier, recorded that 60 per cent of the population caught smallpox and 20 per cent of the population died from it. Those who survived, and many did, were often badly disfigured by scarring, which affected the whole body, including the face.

Jenner's theory was that the pus from the blisters that milk-maids developed on contracting cowpox protected them from smallpox. He tested his hypothesis by inoculating patients with pus from milkmaids infected by cowpox. He wrote it up as a case series of twenty-three patients.

It was all the more remarkable given the lack of understanding about bacteria or viruses, which were only discovered by Louis Pasteur and Robert Koch towards the middle and end of the nineteenth century. Jenner was way ahead of his time. Firstly, he demonstrated that cowpox blisters could be inoculated from person to person, not just cow to milkmaid. Secondly, by exposing his inoculated patients, including his own baby son, to smallpox, he was able to demonstrate that prior cowpox infection conferred a significant degree of protection against smallpox.

That his initial paper of 1796 was not accepted for publication by the *Royal Society* suggests that Jenner's ideas were too radical for his contemporaries. If it wasn't understood, it couldn't be accepted for publication. He followed their advice to collect more data, but avoided the ignominy of possible rejection by publishing his monologue as a scholarly leaflet, and the rest is history.

For Edward Jenner, private practice was an important source of income, particularly in the early stages of his career as a country doctor in rural Gloucestershire. He would ride by horse at any time of the day or night when summoned to see a patient, through whatever weather greeted him, and then lay on hands and do the doctoring. He expected to be paid for his efforts. Jenner's financial situation improved towards the end of his career with two huge financial gifts, supported by the king and Parliament: £10,000 in 1802 for his work on vaccination, and a further £20,000 in 1807 (equivalent to well over a million pounds in today's money). These were gifts of gratitude for personal benefit, acknowledging his lifetime's work and the huge service to the nation in devising a treatment to prevent smallpox.

•   •   •

As a result of mass vaccination, smallpox was eradicated in humans in 1980 (the only human viral disease to have ever been fully eradicated). The last naturally occurring case of smallpox occurred in October 1977, 179 years after the publication of Jenner's monologue on smallpox vaccination. Smallpox is estimated to have killed 300 million people in the twentieth century, and 500 million people in the last 100 years of its existence. On reflection, it is striking how science has thus far been able to address and resolve such dangerous threats to humankind. Also notable is the excitement and tenacity of scientists such as Jenner, Gilbert and Osier when faced with these major health hazards which need fixing. How gratifying for Jenner and Gilbert to play their part in these great advances in science: vaccination against small pox and COVID, gaining widespread acceptance in their lifetimes, validation of their life's work. Jenner was correctly feted in his own lifetime for his research success, as will be Gilbert and others who developed COVID vaccines more than 200 years later.

•   •   •

NIA, THIRTEEN, BLISTERS ON HANDS

Nia's mum: 'Nia and her sister were both given baby calves at the beginning of June.'

AA: 'What did you call your calf, Nia?'

Nia: 'Violet.'

Nia's mum: 'Two or three days after being given them, the two calves became unwell.'

Nia: 'They were off their food and went floppy. They wouldn't stand up. We had to feed them with a bottle, but they weren't interested'

Nia's mum: 'Within a couple of days Nia developed itchy raised bumps on the backs of her fingers and hands. We went to see the GP, who diagnosed impetigo (a bacterial infection of the skin). We then took photos and shared them with close farming friends via social media. Within a few hours, a friend of a friend had shown the photos and told the story to a vet in York. The vet in York thought it was cowpox, which I then relayed back to the GP.'

AA: 'How did you feel, Nia?'

Nia's mum: 'She was a bit off-colour for a few days, but not too bad. The blisters were driving her mad, very itchy, but they only lasted for a few days, then burst and went crusty.'

AA: 'How is Violet now?'

Nia: 'She's better.'

I examined Nia's hands. Whatever it was, it was getting better. Nia's mum showed me a sequence of photos on her mobile phone. The photos were typical for cowpox, quite inflamed and sore-looking blisters on the fingers and hands. Nasty and troublesome for a few days, but basically a fairly mild, self-limiting viral infection in humans, contracted from cattle. This was the first case of cowpox I had ever seen. I gave advice and prescribed creams to help to restore the integrity of her skin.

AA: 'One last thing. Would it be possible to send me those photos of Nia's hands, so we can present her case at our local dermatology clinical meeting for teaching purposes?'

Nia's mum: 'Of course.'

AA: 'And a photo of Violet too?'

Nia's mum: 'No problem.'

CHAPTER 22

THE MANY FACES OF THE MEDICAL PROFESSION

2015-2020

Medical students tend to roll their eyes and groan when asked, 'What are you going to specialise in?' Most have no idea; even becoming a doctor seems unreal to some of them. How are they supposed to know what they will specialise in? I didn't.

One day I find myself in clinic with two young medical students who will be with me for two weeks. This is the only dermatology teaching they will receive, enough to pass their exams. More importantly, they will also have a better understanding of what dermatologists do, an insight into why dermatology is now so popular as a career choice for junior doctors. My hope with each pair of students is that they will enjoy their two weeks of dermatology, learning about skin disease by seeing what we do and listening to the patients' stories. Some might even start to think about becoming dermatologists themselves – or so I hope.

I try to ensure that each pair of students has a rounded experience, putting into practice my teaching skills learnt in Cardiff: using their first names; positioning them in front of the patients, alongside me, included as active participants in the group dynamic; taking an interest in them as individuals; asking them how medical school is going. I enjoy hearing their views about each patient, and like it when they showed an interest in dermatology. In time together away from the clinic, we talk about what makes a career in medicine interesting and rewarding. When discussing career choices, I suggest that they should trust their instincts, and aim for what they can see themselves enjoying and doing well. This is why placements and role models are so important: we are not just here to teach medicine. Placements are an opportunity for students to take a look at different disciplines; they can see what type of doctor ends up doing each specific job. I also like to highlight that clinical medicine alone may not be enough to sustain a career, and keep them happy and fulfilled; they might need something else, such as teaching, research, leadership, academic publishing or management.

For these two students, I explain that each of these is a specialised topic in its own right, requiring a new set of skills and deeper knowledge. They seem surprised to discover that they could mix various ingredients to create a hybrid career. If they choose wisely, they could take on roles that complement each other. In this way their career could keep building, with regular renewal, and will rarely be boring or repetitive. I explain that it was only through taking on additional roles that I was able to reflect on my own character and attributes, and to grow as an individual. Self-awareness, emotional intelligence and emotional growth are attributes I have worked hard to acquire as I have tried to become a better doctor. However, they do not come easily; reading, discussion, reflection and study are all needed. Of these additional roles, I tell these two students, research is the most difficult to do outside a university academic department, even more so in primary care than in hospital practice. Nevertheless, research is still possible as an NHS doctor.

Students sometimes ask me why I have dedicated so much of my career to research. I can give a number of reasons. Experience in research is helpful for clinical practice; it helps to create better doctors. A research degree brings with it transferable skills and insights which can be utilised throughout a medical career; my research degree was the springboard for a career as a clinical academic. Research also paves the way for crucial scientific breakthroughs; Sarah Gilbert had been researching vaccines for a long time when suddenly she was the right person to deliver a COVID vaccine. Research activity is also good for the profile and reputation of the department, never a bad thing. Research is good for the profile of the hospital as it seeks to attract and retain high quality staff and to perform at the highest level possible. Finally, research has the potential to improve patient care. In other words, medical research concerns us all and is essential as we strive to improve health and healthcare.

We often then have a broader discussion about how medical research leads to improvements in healthcare and contributes in a positive way to achieving a healthier and more productive society. Here I like to mention research into high blood pressure by the GP Dr Julian Tudor Hart, who was the first doctor to routinely measure every patient's blood pressure and was therefore able to reduce early death from the complications of raised blood pressure in high-risk patients by 30 per cent. He was awarded the inaugural Discovery Prize by the Royal College of General Practitioners in 2006.

Another role I mention is medical educator. The NHS is full of students; there are many opportunities for teaching, so why not acquire the knowledge and skills to be good at it? Most doctors start teaching as junior doctors, although they may start sooner than this. Peer-to-peer education is now the norm, where students teach each other. A formal teaching qualification is highly desirable for doctors who wish to build a career as a medical educator, and enhances their CV for career progression. As with anything else, knowledge, skills, behaviours and attitudes must be acquired in order to be excellent as a medical educator. Enthusiasm and a deep knowledge of clinical medicine are not enough in themselves. Some doctors fail to recognise this, and may even miss out due to their lack of formal training.

Clinical leadership is another role that is interesting and important. My experience of hospital managers has been positive. I explain to students that medical management is a career like any other. It requires intelligence, know how, passion and dedication. Like the doctors and nurses, our managers are doing their best in a challenging environment; they learn not to take things personally if exposed to aggression and negativity from doctors. The best managers are energetic, positive and well-organised; they coax consultants to engage, by helping them to understand performance figures and finances for their clinical service. Doctors who are remote from NHS decision-makers often suggest two solutions for service underperformance: more staff and more money (to pay existing staff to do more). I explain to the students that the cash-strapped NHS requires a more sophisticated approach. I like to hear what the students think on these matters (most have not given it much thought). Students are sometimes surprised to hear that the solution to a service's woes may be to change how they work. To prevail in the NHS requires clarity of purpose; what are we trying to do? What job does the patient need us to do? Additionally, there needs to be strategic thinking, strong leadership and teamwork.

There are two complementary elements to doctors and health-care management: the first is how doctors interact with their managers; the second is doctors themselves working as managers through clinical leadership. I explain to the medical students that some doctors have an affinity to health care management and become excellent leaders, whilst others loathe it and try not to be involved. For those who like management it may start with being the clinical lead for a speciality. Other opportunities for doctors to gain experience in management are to join a trust committee; in time this might progress to being committee chairperson, or perhaps an associate medical director. Some doctors relish these leadership roles, and the chance to lead others and influence how healthcare is delivered. Some go further, progressing to executive level by becoming medical director or even chief executive for their NHS trust or health board. As with everything else in medicine, these management roles are time consuming and usually require doing less clinical medicine. I tell the students that this is reconciled each year at job planning.

Students are often unaware that the best performing health care organisations in the UK have clinicians in key leadership positions. I illustrate this for students by describing examples of trusts and organisations that are doing well. For example, when visiting the Royal United Hospitals (RUH) in Bath to hear about their clinical leadership, I spoke to Lisa Lewis, head of their programme for change called 'Improving Together'.

According to Lisa, in 2017 it became clear that ongoing pressures on the local health system, the ambitions of NHS Five Year Forward View and the expectations of RUH stakeholders would require much more from the hospital. The RUH set out to address these challenges by establishing an environment where every member of staff would be engaged meaningfully as a problem-solver working together towards reconciling these competing pressures. The goal was to create a platform of standardised work and governance where continuous improvement and transformational change would be successfully implemented, embedded and sustained.

A team of senior managers and clinicians from Bath visited Western Sussex Hospitals NHS Foundation Trust to learn more about their recently implemented whole-system transformation. They had used a tried-and-tested approach to organisational development based on Lean methodology. The team reported back to the RUH executive board, who decided to support their recommendation. KPMG, a multinational professional services company, were employed for twelve months at the start of this change programme to help the trust to embed the methodology. The RUH is now in the third of a four-year roll-out programme. Although some clinical teams were faster to embrace the programme than others, none have rejected this change in practice. Furthermore, as more teams were trained, there was an acceleration in the overall performance for the whole organisation. Of course, the pandemic did not help with the roll-out of this new way of working; nevertheless, without these changes the response to the pandemic would have been more difficult. This story of transformational change reminded me of our own situation in dermatology in North Wales, where our newly changed service proved so nimble when adapting to the new reality of health care in a pandemic.

* * *

I am always impressed by the fourth-year Cardiff University medical students who join me for teaching in North Wales and appear well equipped to cope with the professional challenges ahead. They arrive with the analytical skills needed for intuitive medicine and problem-solving; keyboard and computer skills honed at work and play since infancy; advanced communication skills; a good understanding of the need for empathy and kindness in their patient care; the ability to search for and use information; a clear understanding of reflective practice, nurtured and developed since year one at medical school; great social awareness about the need for inclusivity and equality in society and the importance of avoiding any form of discrimination; a strong understanding and commitment to team working.

At the core of learning to be a good doctor is professionalism: a set of attitudes, beliefs and behaviours that underpin good clinical practice and all aspects of patient care. Understanding what is meant by professionalism in the context of being a doctor is a lifelong challenge. We are the second most trusted professional group in the UK (after nurses), a position earned by doctors taking these issues seriously.

My own understanding of professionalism was greatly enhanced by teaching this topic to third-year medical students in Cardiff. I started by trying to give a lecture on the subject. Within minutes I had lost the audience: twenty-five medical students in the boardroom at the University Hospital of Wales in Cardiff; not one of them listening. My next attempt was more successful: I asked the students to prepare a five-minute presentation on a successful doctor, highlighting their professionalism. I suggested that the students should pick subjects from the long obituaries in the *British Medical Journal*. This worked well as a teaching and learning experience; the students were more engaged, and my role became the moderator. However, multiple presentations about highly successful doctors (nearly all of the long obituaries in the *BMJ* are for doctors with successful careers) was dull; these successful doctors seldom had lapses in their professionalism. Something was missing in these sessions.

I then came up with the idea of students having the option to present examples of professional lapses by using the fitness to practice tribunal reports from the General Medical Council website. The students much preferred discussing doctors who had ended up in trouble with the GMC than the successful doctors from the *BMJ* obituaries. They were often shocked by the professional lapses that these doctors had shown, and were more hawkish than the GMC in terms of sanctions and penalties for the offending doctors. These sessions often became animated, as the students took positions and expressed their views. The feedback from this teaching was strongly positive; we ended up capturing it in a simple questionnaire study and published our findings in a medical education journal. However, it never seemed to occur to these third-year medical students that one or two of them might eventually end up in trouble with the GMC themselves. I finished these sessions by summarising what had been covered, and then describing my own view of professionalism as something organic and delicate inside each of us that requires care and attention. If we are conscientious, and pay close attention, our professionalism can be encouraged to grow into something vigorous, healthy and robust. If we ignore our professionalism, it will wither and die.

In the 2014 Reith Lectures, Dr Atul Gawande addressed 'The Future of Medicine'. He started by considering why doctors fail, and then described 'the system' and the need for it to change by making what has been invisible visible. According to Gawande, 'We need to remove the veil around what happens in that procedure room, in that clinic, in that office or in that hospital.' He acknowledges that it is uncomfortable looking inside our fallibility. He went on to highlight the problem with hubris in doctors, before concluding with a lecture on the idea of well-being. I was excited to share Atul Gawande's insights with my son Ben, then in his fourth year at medical school, only to have him tell me that he had heard them already.

'We were advised to listen to them in our first year at medical school,' he said.

How times have changed, and yet in medicine, so much remains the same. Abraham Verghese describes this with clarity in his novel *Cutting for Stone,* a book about Indian doctors working in a mission hospital in Ethiopia in the late 1950s. It reminded me of my own passion for learning medicine. The doctors in this novel are dedicated and inspired by their calling to medicine. Their experiences were similar to my own when learning medicine as a postgraduate student in York and Middlesbrough in the late 1980s. The fundamentals were the same, with professionalism at the core. In contrast, A. J. Cronin's book *The Citadel* covers the darker aspects of a medical career. The fictional hero, Dr Andrew Manson, started out as an idealistic young doctor in the South Wales Valleys, serving a mining community and revelling in his duties (being Scottish, interested in research, and working with the mining communities in South Wales he was not so very different from the young Archie Cochrane). He ends up as a GP working in London, seduced by money earned from private practice and unrecognisable from the person he appeared to be at the start of the story. It is a morality tale, but vividly highlights the best aspects of professionalism, and what happens to doctors who neglect it.

One element of professionalism concerns listening to our patients, and acting as their advocate and advisor. Dr Vivek H. Murthy, the 19th Surgeon General of the United States from 2014–2017, highlighted the need to listen to patients in his book *Togetherness.* It's become increasingly evident that many patients are suffering from loneliness. Furthermore, loneliness may also be an issue among healthcare professionals, as it is for patients. Murthy creates a compelling case for practicing medicine in a joined-up and integrated way, looking out for each other and making sure to consider the possibility of loneliness in our colleagues and in our patients. This resonated with me, the system we introduced in North Wales having integration and joined-up working at its core.

Loneliness is much more common than we might think; the first step for doctors when dealing with loneliness in others is to recognise that it exists, but may not be overt or easy to identify. Murthy's book was timely, published immediately before the pandemic, which created much more loneliness around the world. We are now more aware of loneliness in society, and appreciate the need to develop new ways of living which keep us better connected to each other. But for loneliness to be tackled effectively, society as a whole must change. Indeed, it has never been more important to reconsider the fundamentals of patient interaction and to develop healthcare systems that address the issue of loneliness. Where are we now going with health care generally as we emerge from the global pandemic?

· · ·

WOMAN, AGED TWENTY-EIGHT, RED SPOT ON CHEEK

'It's a spider naevus, not a basal cell carcinoma,' I explain.

'What's a spider naevus? I hate spiders!'

'It's not a real spider. It's a small red skin lesion consisting of a collection of blood vessels with a passing resemblance to a spider. If you press gently on the body of the spider, the legs disappear. When you release the pressure, the spider naevus reappears, body first, and then the legs. It is a minor abnormality in a superficial skin blood vessel.'

'How can I get rid of it? It's ugly.'

'Laser,' I reply.

CHAPTER 23

CLAYTON CHRISTENSEN AND THE BUSINESS OF HEALTHCARE

2011–2015

As a firm believer in Bevan's NHS, I was surprised by my reaction to the American bestseller on medical practice, *The Innovator's Prescription: A Disruptive Solution for Health Care* by Clayton Christensen. Although written primarily for the American healthcare system, it contains much that is relevant to our NHS. If healthcare systems reflect a country's society, we know that the American healthcare system reflects deep-seated and ingrained inequality as well as extraordinary inconsistency. The USA spends by far the greatest proportion of GDP on health care for any developed country, as well as having the world's highest per capita health expenditure. What does this huge spend achieve? The best five-year survival figures for breast and prostate cancer in the world, with second and fourth best for lung cancer and colon cancer. What a contrast to discover that USA is eighteenth out of eighteen for life expectancy at birth, perinatal mortality and survival from ischaemic stroke. In some instances, theirs is the best healthcare in the world; in others, the US barely reaches third world standards. And yet *The Innovator's Prescription* was a revelation for the insights it provided into the business of healthcare, and the solutions it offered in terms of making healthcare more effective and better for patients and governments.

The prospect of meeting Christensen, a lecturer on the leadership and innovation course run by Harvard Medical School, was an exciting one. The course had been recommended by a number of colleagues from the Faculty of Medical Education at Cardiff University. I had *Escape Fire* as my reading for the flight to Boston, the collected speeches of Don Berwick to the Institute for Healthcare Improvement. Berwick was well known to me on account of his evangelical leadership of the Institute for Healthcare Improvement. His quality improvement philosophy was gaining traction around the world, including within the NHS in Wales. I was excited to be heading for Christensen and Berwick's home city. I also shared common purpose with

William Osler, who 120 years before me had visited Boston regularly to find out the best way to teach students and to run a medical school. The timing in terms of attending the course couldn't have been better; my healthcare organisation, the Aneurin Bevan Health Board, was going through significant changes, in a move to reconfigure the whole local healthcare system. Furthermore, the undergraduate course for medicine in Cardiff was also going through a much-needed overhaul. Change was in the air; I was excited by the prospect of playing a leading role. As director of research and development for the health board, and recently appointed lead for the intercalated Bachelor of Science course on medical education at the university, I was well positioned to play a part in the change process in both organisations.

Berwick, a paediatrician, came to prominence through his pioneering work as an advocate for health care change. In the early 1990s, he helped to set up and lead the Institute for Healthcare Improvement; initially a small gathering of a few hundred enthusiasts, it swelled into a large and influential organisation with a sustained positive impact on health care around the world. I was struck by how much Osler, Christensen and Berwick had in common. Each emphasised the importance of a deep understanding of the client/patient as part of their credo. All three galvanised their professional communities through their novel insights and their passion for teaching and nurturing others. They all had the intellect and self-confidence to believe steadfastly in their ideas and insights and not waver when challenged. All three showed the highest level of leadership through their humility and personal modesty. Finally, all three devoted their professional lives to helping others, for the greater good. Berwick, like all of us, was sure to have been strongly influenced by the legacy of Osler. Indeed, Berwick was the quintessential Oslerian doctor, advocating kindness, compassion, common sense, and a humanistic approach to doctoring. Berwick and Christensen were on contrasting paths, but their approach to healthcare had interesting similarities: to focus more strongly on better understanding how healthcare works for each of our patients, and to focus on creating efficient systems and eradicating waste.

Don Berwick's style was to use his patient-centered clinical practice to draw wider parallels across the whole of health care. As for William Osler, Berwick also built his approach to medicine on foundations of patient-centered care. Berwick's paper on patient-centered care published in the journal *Health Affairs* in 2009 has nearly 1,000 citations (this means that nearly 1,000 authors have referenced this paper in their own writings), a huge number for a discursive paper. His mantra was: 'reduce waste in all its forms; study and apply the principle of continuous flow; reduce demand; plot measurements of healthcare performance over time (to generate discussion and debate rather than to be reductionist); match capacity to demand; cooperate with each other; never lose sight of the patient as the central figure'. For the non-medic, this may all sound like common sense, which it is. But that is what is so appealing about Berwick.

In 1993, Berwick had an epiphany, described in the opening to his speech to the fifth annual National Forum on Quality Improvement in Healthcare: 'Perhaps like me you look back over the years to certain key moments when some event changed your mind forever. Before the event, you saw things one way; afterward, irrevocably, you saw things differently. These are moments of change. Let me tell you two such moments for me.' Berwick then described two inspiring stories of dedication in the pursuit of excellence, one from the National Air and Space Agency (NASA) and one from Berwick's own clinical practice. Berwick went on: 'Why do we care so much? We care because we feel that it is our duty to do so. It is our craft. But this sense of duty does not come from outside; it arises from within. No reward can create this caring. It can be driven out of us, but it cannot be driven into us.'

Berwick's efforts have inspired the medical profession around the world to work together as we try to improve healthcare. For example, in my own hospital in North Wales, a popular and inspiring consultant is Dr Chris Subbe. His health improvement work uses methodology developed by Berwick's Institute for Healthcare Improvement. Chris has focused on early recognition and treatment for sepsis, a life-threatening condition if overlooked or diagnosed late. Chris has become a national figure in the UK for this work, now supported by significant grant funding. Importantly, this work saves lives. It is an extraordinary achievement for Berwick, a paediatrician from Boston, to have his ideas on healthcare be picked up by my colleague Chris and many others like him around the globe. Donald Berwick was knighted in 2005 for his work in creating new care models in five trusts in the National Health Service.

Berwick has had key medical leadership roles, including two years heading Medicare and Medicaid, the safety net healthcare providers in the US for the elderly and the poor. He led the national advisory group on the safety of patients in England, which reported to England's Department of Health in the wake of the Stafford Hospital scandal in the late 2000s. This scandal concerned poor care and high mortality rates in patients at Stafford Hospital, and resulted in a full public enquiry chaired by Robert Frances QC, which reported finally in February 2013 with 290 recommendations. Berwick's brief was to draw lessons from this scandal, and to make recommendations to the NHS as a whole on what to do next. Berwick advised that new policies must be scientifically grounded and should include what was known already about the dynamics of patient safety. He anticipated that the NHS would take big steps towards improvement once established practice had been modified. He emphasised that health care improvement is an on-going process which is never done, and that change must take place across the entire NHS so that safety continually improves. This recommendation was picked up by my own health board with the creation of a clinical service improvement unit, called 'Aneurin Bevan Continuous Improvement' (ABCi).

By following the footsteps of Osler's visits to Boston at the end of the nineteenth century, and Berwick as a medical student and paediatrician, I was seeking answers to fundamental questions about medicine and medical education, such as how to make my own clinical practice as a dermatologist more effective, more efficient, timelier, and more accessible.

Back in Boston. Day one. The first talk was by Clay Christensen, the author of *The Innovator's Prescription*. He was an academic at Harvard Business School whose research had focused originally on the world of business before expanding into the business of healthcare.

'Making healthcare affordable and accessible is a challenge of monstrous proportions; far beyond the most intractable of the problems I had previously tried to study,' he told us.

Christensen went on to explain his interest in understanding why great firms fail – the inspiration for his first book, *The Innovator's Dilemma*. He and his colleagues had identified a consistent pattern in the failure of successful firms. Year on year, these firms focused on better products for their best and most profitable clients, often to the point of over-engineering. They did this because the profit margins were high and they already had the clients. This focus blinded them to the threat of poorly capitalised upstarts offering cheaper products at the bottom end of the market. In time, such upstarts became a threat as they started to be profitable and move upmarket. Christensen explained to us that the upstarts typically incorporated three elements in their strategy: a technological enabler, a business model innovation, and a value network. The term Christensen and his colleagues coined for this phenomenon was 'disruptive innovation'. It was simple and easy to understand. It all made sense and rang true; we were hooked.

Christensen used many examples to illustrate his theory, including personal computers. Prior to the 1970s, there were only a few thousand people in the world who could design and operate mainframe computers. The business model required gross profit margins of 60 per cent just to cover the overheads. The personal computer changed this, creating computers that were mass-produced and affordable to all. The technological enabler for this disruption was the microprocessor. However, the microprocessor was not, in itself, enough to create disruption. Both

IBM and Digital Equipment Corporation (DEC) had microprocessors. Whilst DEC eschewed business model innovation, IBM set up a separate and independent business far away from its main computer business units. In this new personal computer business model, IBM could make money with low margins, low overhead costs, and high unit volumes. In contrast, DEC could not compete and were swept away. Thus, Christensen's theory required both a technological enabler, in this case the microprocessor, and a low-cost innovative business model; the third element was an economically coherent value network. In this example, the value network was the huge, untapped demand from the public for affordable computers.

Christensen routinely focused on trying to understand what patients *really* want out of healthcare. He challenged the audience, 120 doctors from around the globe, whether any of us knew what job our patients really wanted to get done through their attendance in our clinics? He highlighted that understanding this was integral to shared decision-making, a process which starts by the doctor asking the patient what they really want, which brought the conversation back to Berwick and Osler (and my GP trainer Dr Gerry Jackson), who all emphasised the imperative to keep patients' needs central to the doctoring process.

On the final day of the course, Christensen spoke about innovation in health care. Christensen emphasised the importance of understanding our patients and making sure that services addressed the jobs that patients were seeking to get done. Now, he was applying this analytical framework to the business of healthcare. We discussed the complexity of modern hospitals and the difficulty in reconciling service delivery with diverse business models operating at the same time in the same institution. We discussed streamlined, highly efficient, protocol-driven one-stop shops run by nurses and contrasted them with 'solution shops' where intuitive medicine required highly trained doctors, sophisticated tests and specialised investigations.

I came away understanding that there were two jobs that patients needed doing: firstly, to know and understand what the problem was; secondly, for the treatment of the problem to be effective, timely, and convenient. Whilst there might be a tension between these two jobs, making them hard to reconcile, according to Christensen, the solution is to separate solution shops from value-added processes in healthcare. In other words, the complex, difficult, intuitive part of patient care needs to be separated from the straightforward process-driven side of health care. Christensen explained that value-adding processes become more cost effective and productive when a production line mentality is adopted. This may sound inappropriate for medicine; however, it can easily be justified by efficiency, reduced costs-per-case, a lower rate of complications, improved safety and higher productivity. To put this into terms that the patient would understand, dedicated value-added processes create services that are effective, timely and convenient; exactly what the patient is seeking in terms of the second job that needs to be done. Additionally, such high throughput services are nearly always cost-effective and affordable.

I would go on to attend the course again, twice, and benefited enormously from interacting with doctors from other disciplines in medicine, and from different healthcare environments. It was refreshing to consider health and healthcare from outside the NHS and outside the dermatology bubble. I was able to reflect on how we were running our services, and to pick up novel ideas to address deeply ingrained health-care problems. Finland, for example, has the highest number of practicing nurses per 1,000 population, and one of the lowest rates of perinatal mortality in the world. Perhaps part of the solution to the UK's many health care challenges was to employ more nurses, and to work differently? This was to be at the centre of our own innovative dermatology service in North Wales ten years later.

A modest man, Christensen undoubtedly had something special about him. I felt humble in his presence and energised by his discourse. He listened with great interest to my stories about health care in the NHS, asking probing questions to better understand the issues. I was reminded that those with the most brilliant minds are sometimes able to communicate their insights in the most simple and understandable ways.

●　●　●

FEMALE, FORTY-SEVEN, ON CANCER FAST-TRACK

Brenda is worried. Her index fingernail, left hand, has recently turned black. It is also smelly. She asked her GP, who said it might be a nail melanoma. He photographed it, and said the response from dermatology would be quick. It was. Nevertheless, she still has time to look up nail melanoma on Google. Brenda works out that she might be dead by Christmas.

She explains to me, 'The nail has gradually become detached. As you can see, I manicure my nails carefully, but it has been increasingly hard to clean under this nail, as the nail became more and more detached. It has been smelly for a few months, and then turned black about four weeks ago.'

I examine the offending nail. About 60 per cent of the nail is now detached, from the far end to about one third of the way from the posterior nail fold. The affected nail looks fairly normal, except for the black and yellow colours on the underside. Where the nail is still attached, it is pink and normal-looking.

'We call this onycholysis,' I declare. 'The nail has become detached due to excessive manicuring. Water gets trapped under the nail, which has encouraged the growth of bacteria and fungi. The recent black change is due to mould. That's why it smells.'

'Gross!' says Brenda. 'Is there anything to be done?'

'Cut the nail as short as possible and keep it short. The smell will go quickly, as will the black mould. In time, the nail should reattach as it grows out.'

CHAPTER 24

TACKLING THE WAITING LISTS

2018–2019

I had never worked in a department with short waiting lists, so could only imagine what it might be like. I had visions of patients who were grateful to have gained fast access to the service, and were complimentary about the care they had received from hard-working doctors and nurses; I guessed that the clinical team would be more fulfilled in their work, seeing more patients with urgent, severe and acute problems, and far fewer with minor complaints and benign skin lesions; I anticipated that the dermatology clinic clerks and secretaries would no longer be subjected to multiple phone calls each day from disgruntled patients on the waiting list, many abusive and rude; I hoped that demands on our medical secretaries would reduce and that going to work each day would no longer create an inner sense of dread; finally, I dreamed about the smiling managers' faces as they congratulated the whole team on their outstanding performance in reducing the waiting lists and keeping them short.

To turn this dream into reality required everyone to accept that the current system was not working, and was impacting negatively on staff and patients.

Diary entry, January 2018.

I am struck by the complacency within the health board which has allowed poor performance to become the norm. How to explain this? Our managers are intelligent and well-motivated people, with lots of experience and many personal successes in their careers. The local GPs are some of the best I have worked with. Our three clinical nurse specialists are all superb at their jobs. Our trainee doctors are all gifted and capable doctors with bright futures ahead. Our GPs with a special interest (GPs who work within our department doing dermatology) are high-achieving doctors who have found their niche in dermatology. Our clinic clerks and medical secretaries are hard-working people, who know that their work is important and valuable to the local community. So why is our service failing? Why do we all believe that the current system is worth preserving? Why does everyone think that doing our best is enough, when we know the system isn't working for our patients? Who is to blame? How could this failure be tolerated? What is the explanation for this complacency?

Failure is looking us full in the face, yet we are all in denial, kidding ourselves that the status quo is OK, and that with more resources better performance will follow. It has always been like this; no one ever challenges the failing system. The difference in North Wales is that Betsi (this health board) has been in 'special measures' since 2015, a category reserved for particularly bad performance which has impacted on patient safety. The way out of this failure should be top quality strategic leadership from the executives, with empowered clinical leaders. However, special measures have already been maintained for nearly three years, official confirmation, if it were needed, that the whole organisation is failing. There is absolutely no chance of strategic leadership from our executives.

* * *

When we think about the NHS, what usually springs to mind are the clinicians; the doctors and nurses who interact with patients. However, like athletes in a professional sports team, actors on a stage, or professors in a university, these front-line players are all supported by teams of people who are essential for their success. Healthcare is no different. Our team includes clinic clerks, medical secretaries, managers, pharmacists, nurses, junior doctors and general practitioners. Furthermore, we are supported by accountants, planners, health improvement experts, medical educators, trainers, engineers, IT experts, librarians, refuse collectors, porters, teachers and researchers. These NHS workers were all honoured in July 2021 by the award of a George Cross along with all those who have worked in the NHS since 1948. This award was made to a much-loved NHS that was battered and bruised, but had prevailed in the face of the COVID-19 pandemic.

NHS medical secretaries are key members of clinical teams: they type letters (lots of them), interact with patients by phone, contact GP surgeries, set up meetings, accept ward referrals, interact with the dermatologist on-call and act as the hub of the service, the rest of the team orbiting around them.

Our three secretaries do their best to keep the service going. However, it is often challenging, with too much work and not enough time to do it.

Before Dermatology Integrated Care was introduced in early 2019, Gail, the senior dermatology secretary, worked in a large open-plan office with a spectacular view of the mountains of Snowdonia. Gail was always asking the managers for help; she knew her small clerical team was not coping. Eventually, it became too much for her; she was dreading coming to work. Gail was signed off by her GP with severe anxiety provoked by the stress of her job, and was off for four months. She told me that this was the first time she had ever been off work with stress; she felt ashamed, as if she had failed in her duty and was letting down the rest of the team. When Gail returned to work after this four-month break, she described things as being 'pretty much the same'; however, she felt less stressed and more able to cope.

Kerrie Gallear is the dermatology clinic clerk at the main hospital in Bangor. She has been in her current role for four years, having joined our team when the waiting lists were as bad as they had ever been. I knew Kerrie fairly well as our offices were nearby. I knew that she was devoted to her job, starting work each day soon after 7 a.m., even though she was only paid from 8 a.m. Kerrie had first-hand knowledge about how the service was performing; she was responsible for booking patients into clinics for appointments and was the person whom patients spoke to when confirming that they would attend clinic, or needed to be seen again. Kerrie was also the person who dealt with calls from patients who were on the waiting lists, enquiring about when they would be seen in the clinic.

I decided to find out what Kerrie thought about the long waiting lists and ask her how they impacted on her job. She told me that when the waiting lists were long, the phone rang constantly, all day every day, with disgruntled patients trying to find out when they would be seen. She reported that most patients were polite, but some were rude and aggressive; she received up to five such calls each day. I asked her how this made her feel; 'Angry,' she replied. I asked her how she coped. 'I swear,' she replied. She smiled, as she revealed this secret self, in no way embarrassed or ashamed. I asked her which swear words. 'All of them,' she replied with a grin. We were both laughing now. 'Including the F-word?' I asked. 'Especially the F-word,' she replied.

I was amazed. I had no idea what work was really like for this polite and seemingly well-mannered woman. On reflection, I could have guessed, but had never bothered to consider what it was like to do her work. I stated that I assumed that she would never use bad language when on the phone with patients. 'Correct,' she replied.

Kerrie could see that I was surprised by this conversation. She could also see from my reaction that this revelation made no difference to our working relationship. I was grateful for her honesty, and felt that this exchange had strengthened our bond. I would continue to rely on Kerrie's efficiency, hard work and common sense; Kerrie would continue to be a key person at the centre of our service, making sure we were patient-focused in everything we did without mishaps, omissions or errors. However, something had to be done. By maintaining a system which created this level of abuse from our patients, we were letting Kerrie down.

I asked the trainee dermatologists in my team for their impressions of how our service was functioning. Dr Otilia Azamfirei is a Romanian-trained dermatologist who had joined our team two years earlier. Otilia is married to an ophthalmologist; both are trying to progress their careers whilst bringing up their two children, aged ten and eight. Otilia responded to my question by describing her first clinic at Ysbyty Gwynedd:

'There were eight patients on my clinic list. The first was a man with a nodular malignant melanoma [a very serious form of skin cancer which can kill patients]. I explained the diagnosis and arranged for the melanoma to be excised. Whilst feeling so sorry for that unfortunate guy, I also felt a weird enthusiasm to have joined this dermatology team; yes, I could make a difference here. At last, I could use my knowledge and skills again to help patients. I was excited by this work! By the end of that clinical session, my enthusiasm was already dying: the remaining seven patients included six with seborrhoeic keratoses [benign, age-related skin lesions] which had been inappropriately referred via the fast-track for urgent suspected cancers, and one patient with a rash which had resolved spontaneously during the fourteen-month wait for an appointment. This was going to be my daily routine from now on: lots of patients with trivial skin problems and occasional patients where my expertise was needed.'

Next up were general practitioners; they have a central role in dermatology healthcare, but were distant and remote from the specialist team. A regular aspiration of healthcare reform in the UK in the last thirty years has been to 'bridge the gap between primary and secondary care'. How ironic that the evolution of the NHS in this period has done the opposite, with GPs and hospital specialists now wider apart than ever. What was it like for the GPs managing skin conditions in their patients within the old way of working? This is what they told me:

'I was anxious about patient care in dermatology, knowing the patients would have to wait so long to be seen. This anxiety made me refer earlier and more often. It also made me over-emphasise the urgency so that the patients were seen sooner. It made me game the system.' GP, Conwy.

'Before the system changed, I dreaded seeing patients with skin disease, knowing my dermatology was poor, and they would probably need referral onwards to the specialist. In the back of my mind was the knowledge that the patient in front of me was in for a long wait. If they had a rash, their itching and sleepless nights were sure to have a big impact. There was a sense of hopelessness which could only be expressed by showing compassion for their suffering.' GP, Holyhead.

'When I was a GP trainee two decades ago, a routine dermatology referral meant eighteen months wait for patients.' GP, Bangor.

'Dermatology before the system changed was hard for all of us, particularly the patients. The waiting list for dermatology was so long that by the time patients were seen, some had forgotten why they had been referred, but kept the appointment anyway to ask about their latest skin complaint. Many patients opted to be seen privately. We even had a patient who was sent an appointment by the hospital a few months after they had died [from something else].' GP, Pwllheli.

I also interviewed the dermatology specialist nurses in our team; all three are dedicated and highly effective team members. I asked Rhian how our long waiting lists this made her feel.

'Sad, angry, frustrated, powerless. The worst thing was knowing that these patients are being let down by the system. It seems to me that the referral system is laborious and long-winded. Referral letters from GPs come with a short history and no photos and the patients wait for far too long to be seen. No one really questions it. This is how it has always been. Our team is tiny and we take some pride in doing the best that we can in difficult circumstances with limited resources.'

NHS managers are responsible for running NHS clinical services; they coordinate change when change is needed. Despite being one health board, dermatology at Betsi Cadwaladr University Health Board was managed as three separate services. It was this separation which had enabled our team in West to change our service model by introducing Dermatology Integrated Care, whilst dermatology services elsewhere in the health board carried on with the old way of working. For me, this was helpful, as it allowed direct comparisons to be made about the performance of the new and old models of care. This appealed to my research background, by effectively creating a control group to compare with our change group; it was the same population of patients, with the same GPs, in the same geographical area, within the same health board, in the same part of the NHS, with the same rainy weather. Any differences in performance between the dermatology in West and elsewhere in the health board were best explained by the changed service. Furthermore, colleagues working in the old way remained firmly entrenched; they heard about our changed service, and made it clear that they were not interested in adopting any of our innovations. Had they followed our lead and started working differently, their status as a control group would have no longer been valid, and comparisons would have been difficult.

Our managers empowered and supported our clinical team to proceed with changing the service model without needing to seek approval with the dermatology teams elsewhere in the health board. The prevailing philosophy seemed to be that our service needed to change if we were to survive, and that any consultant trying to rise to this challenge should be supported. Furthermore, the changes that were proposed had no resource implications; no extra money was being sought, which allowed our managers to give the nod of approval without the need for a business case. The plan was to use our resources differently and to change the way of working, and to see if this had a positive effect on patient care.

Alison Kemp was one of three operational managers for dermatology within the health board. She told me that her friends would describe her as being passionate, determined, direct but also approachable. She was a veteran of the regular dermatology health board management meetings following her appointment as an operational manager for the speciality six years earlier. These meetings were managers only, involving service discussion and analysis of performance indicators across the whole health board.

Alison was intrigued by the dermatology service in West: it was smallest in terms of resources, but consistently outperformed the dermatology services in Central and East. It was well known that dermatology in West never breached the critical service deadlines set by NHS Wales, whereas breaches were a regular occurrence for dermatology services elsewhere in the health board. The explanation for this, Alison found out, was that the managers in West worked closely with their consultants and developed trusting and harmonious relationships. Alison recognised the need to make the most of existing resources as the economic climate within the health board meant that no more would be forthcoming. However, for some of her clinical services, the clinicians were insistent of the need for more resource to solve their service delivery issues. This impasse created friction between the clinicians and the managers, characterised eventually by finger-pointing and acrimony. Despite this, after twenty-five years as a health service manager, Alison remained passionate about her job; she was committed to doing the right thing for patient care and using NHS resources wisely. She was also frustrated by the resistance to change within the NHS:

'There never seems to be much thinking about doing things differently. I am sometimes disappointed by the lack of patient perspective in health care.'

Eleri Roberts was also an NHS operational service manager, working in West, our part of the health board. Her first language was Welsh, easy to spot by the cadences and lyrical nature of her English sentence construction. Whilst being cheerful and outgoing, Eleri had a strong personality with inner steel. Like Alison Kemp, Eleri managed a number of clinical services, including dermatology. Eleri described herself as an optimist, always looking for the positives in any situation. Although managing dermatology in the West was always a challenge, it was clear that Eleri derived personal satisfaction from using her skills to eke out the maximum performance from the resources at her disposal; dermatology in West never breached the dead-lines because Eleri made sure it never breached. There was also pride from doing this with a small and harmonious team.

But Eleri, like everyone else in the health board, had low expectations for our under-resourced service. Like Alison Kemp, Eleri knew there was no funding for more resources. The only way to improve the poor performance of the dermatology service in West was to do things differently. Like Alison, Eleri was attracted to the idea of innovation and service change, as long as there was broad support amongst the relevant clinicians. Eleri was also keen on the concept of strategy, where the ambition for change was defined, and the steps to achieve it were clear and realistic. Eleri had insight into what could be achieved by innovation through her experiences of managing rheuma-tology. As with dermatology, the rheumatology service within the health board included three separate services, one of which was under-resourced yet, paradoxically, significantly outper-formed the other two services. Eleri had worked closely with the consultant rheumatologist who had made this service change; she understood the possibility of transforming care by doing things differently. When I explained that I too wanted to do things differently to create a better service, Eleri was support-ive. The key outcome that she would use to assess Dermatology Integrated Care, this new way of working, would be its effect on NHS waiting lists.

This was the context to the change that followed.

*   *   *

TWELVE-YEAR-OLD GIRL
WITH BLEEDING SPOT ON NECK

Katie is twelve. She had picked at a spot on the back of the neck until it bled. Mum put a plaster on it. Then Katie picked at it again. This went on for a couple of weeks. She now has a little, raised, jelly-like red lump at the site which bleeds on contact. The GP asked Katie's mum for a photo, and referred Katie for a teledermatology opinion. Now here she is, a few days later, in the dermatology clinic. The average age in this one-stop-clinic is about eighty. Katie seems pleased to be within this mature cohort.

'It's a pyogenic granuloma,' I explain. 'A benign lump of healing tissue, which will bleed and keep causing Katie trouble.'

'What can you do about it?' mum asks.

An hour later, the Emla local anaesthetic cream has worked. My colleague Maria has gained Katie's confidence for a minor surgical procedure. The prick from the local anaesthetic is hardly felt, says Katie. The pyogenic granuloma is curetted off and the skin cauterised to stop bleeding; end of saga.

'One last thing!' says Maria, raising a finger and locking eyes with Katie. 'Don't pick at it, or you'll be back to see us again!'

CHAPTER 25

BUILDING GP CONFIDENCE

2018–2019

Don Berwick

Dr Bethan Jones was the local lead for general practice in our area for two days each week; the rest of the time she was a GP at Bron Derw, a dynamic group practice in Bangor. Bethan was excellent at weighing up options as she sought solutions to our health care problems. She had lots of roles and responsibilities, but was always upbeat and positive, never flustered. We hit it off, and soon forged a close and supportive working relationship. Together we decided to introduce change, based on the model I had piloted already on Anglesey with Bethan's predecessor Dr Steve MacVicar. We had already assessed the idea of GPs and specialists working together; we knew that it was popular with the GPs as well as the specialist team. Initial feedback from the meetings between the GPs and the specialist team had been positive; both groups said this was time well spent. On the basis of this pilot scheme, we launched Dermatology Integrated Care meetings across Anglesey, Gwynedd and Conwy, thirty-five GP surgeries serving a local population of just under 250,000 people. Here we explained that the new way of working had four principal features:

Specialists and generalists working together as one team.

Teledermatology (the use of clinical photographs with referral letters) for allocating patients to appropriate clinical pathways.

Advice and guidance letters from the specialist team to patients and GPs to avoid some hospital appointments.

Dermatology treatment hubs to be developed in the community, closer to the patients.

'The ambition is to improve local dermatology services, and to reduce patient waiting times.' That was what we said; the reality was that we had no money and very limited resources. I knew from my experience of working in South Wales that there was lots of resource locked into the system. If you want to access resources, all you need to do is to work differently; in other words, to use existing resources differently. This was exactly what Don Berwick and Clay Christensen would have advised me, had I been able to ask them. It was a defining moment, as we were proposing a radical change from the existing service. We knew that this was putting a positive spin on our proposed changes, but we really did believe that dermatology healthcare in our area would change for the better. At its core was the concept of GPs and specialists working together. We wanted GPs to gain in confidence to enable them to better manage the common skin conditions. The GPs would now become part of our team, with good lines of communication and easy access to the hospital specialists. Most importantly, we wanted to get to know each other, to build trust and understanding.

The GPs were sent a document which described the new face-to-face meetings with the specialist team; they were offered the opportunity to host a meeting in their surgeries. When invited, members of the specialist team would pitch up at the GP health centre a few weeks later for the two-hour meeting. I was reminded of my time as a GP trainee in York, and enjoyed reacquainting myself with GP-land.

The first meeting took place at the Parc Glas Surgery on Anglesey, a group practice with three partners. All three GPs attended, one of whom was still on maternity leave but didn't want to miss this meeting (baby came too). Another GP from a neighbouring practice joined us; she was married to one of the three GPs. It was the first time we had met so I started by explaining the concept of this collaborative approach. They in turn told me how dermatology looked from their perspective. We discussed skin photography, teledermatology referrals (GP referral letters with clinical photographs), skin minor surgery in primary care, and then some questions about skin conditions they wanted to know more about.

The meeting finished with four of their patients joining us for consultations; I listened to each of their stories and examined their skin. The patients clearly benefited from being seen by five doctors and a nurse at the same time. With each case a lively discussion ensued. Including patients as a part of the meeting had been an afterthought, but turned out to be a masterstroke; the GPs were learning dermatology through the medium of their own patients, in their own practice. They also liked seeing me in action; it was an opportunity to consider their patients through fresh eyes, and to assess my interpersonal patient and doctoring skills. What did I ask, see and do that they had not? Could they do any of this themselves? I left after nearly two hours, tired but elated. The GPs were positive about the concept of Dermatology Integrated Care and keen to host a return visit in twelve months' time.

The next meeting was in a larger group practice at Llanfairpwll Health Centre just over the Britannia Bridge on Anglesey, where six of the GPs had Welsh as their first language and one was from Macedonia.

'We want to do more dermatology ourselves, but none of us feel confident to do so,' Dr Endaf ap Ieuan said.

I knew he was keen to become better at lesion recognition; he had arranged to join me in my clinic in Llandudno a few weeks earlier to gain experience in dermoscopy (the use of a high powered, illuminated magnifying device for helping to improve diagnoses with skin lesions).

'Should we be learning how to do dermoscopy?' he asked me.

'Yes, it's a good idea. A few GPs in this area are already doing dermoscopy. It has become clear to me that this usually leads to better quality referrals,' I replied. 'Furthermore, some GPs are photographing skin lesions via their dermatoscope, which greatly enhances our ability to diagnose skin lesions from GP referral letters.'

One of the GPs wanted to know more about skin photography: 'Can we use our phones for skin photography, and do we need to ask the patients for signed consent?' she asked.

'Yes,' I replied, 'you can use your own phone, but only if you are using a special app designed for the purpose. The General Medical Council have clear guidance on doctors using their own phones for skin photography.' I told the GPs about the two apps that I knew about that were GMC-compatible. 'Consent is also important. The photograph is part of the medical record and must be treated as such,' I explained. 'This means consent must be sought, and the photo must be stored as part of the patient record by GPs and by the hospital.' I admitted to the GPs that we ourselves were only just getting our act together to do this.

Another GP asked me about skin minor surgery; 'Are we GPs permitted to remove skin cancers?' he asked.

'Yes,' I replied, 'so long as you follow NICE guidance and can demonstrate your competency to do so.' I went on to explain to the GPs our plan to recruit a GP with particular expertise in skin cancer surgery to lead on this in our area. We were hoping to create a network of GP skin surgeons across our patch, all trained to the same high standard and following the same set of clinical guidelines. 'Maybe one of you would like to join this initiative?' I asked.

Dr Manon Williams wanted to learn more about patient access to ultraviolet light therapy. 'It's a great treatment, but sometimes the patients have to wait ages before they can start treatment,' she commented.

'Yes, it's a problem we are aware of, and have recently addressed by setting up a fast-track route for repeat phototherapy courses,' I said. 'In other words, if a patient has previously had phototherapy, and it was a success, they can have repeat courses without the need to be re-referred and seen again in clinic. We call this the "phototherapy fast track".'

Dr Rhys Griffiths, the senior partner, was also interested in minor surgery, and asked about removing benign skin lesions in primary care; he was the lead for skin surgery within the practice. We finished by seeing patients in their large treatment room.

There were four patients with a range of common skin complaints: a teenage girl with acne; a fifty-year-old man with psoriasis; an elderly man with sun-damaged skin; a young woman with an odd-looking mole. These patients were ideal as teaching cases; a range of useful issues and teaching points came up with each patient. Our nurses contributed too: Allyson talked about the treatment of acne. She explained to the GPs that this patient had exhausted the conventional treatments for acne and now needed treatment with isotretinoin tablets. She told the GPs how helpful it was for us at the hospital when GPs anticipated this treatment, and sorted out contraception in their female patients before referring to us.

'Isotretinoin is a potent teratogen and can cause severe birth defects in babies,' Allyson told them, 'so contraception is essential in women treated with this drug during their reproductive years. By convention we usually recommend a hormonal contraceptive as well as a barrier method,' she said.

'Is there anything else we need to do in primary care when referring such patients for isotretinoin therapy?' asked one of the female GPs.

'Yes,' replied Allyson, 'it's really helpful if you have already done the baseline blood tests and have also given the patient a patient information leaflet on isotretinoin to read carefully before they see us in the clinic.'

Rhian Ellis, another of our nurses, then talked about how to treat the elderly man with sun-damaged skin. A sheep farmer all of his life, he'd spent most daylight hours outside in the sun with his dogs.

'Have you ever worn sunscreen when working?' said Rhian.

'No,' came the answer. 'Never.'

Rhian explained that the rough, scaly areas on his face were a form of sun damage called actinic keratoses. She mentioned a patient information leaflet, which one of the GPs found and printed off as she was speaking. Rhian then looked to me to explain the approach to treatment.

'There is a therapeutic ladder we tend to follow for treating actinic keratoses,' I explained. 'Firstly, it is important that the patient understands the diagnosis and prevents further damage from occurring by behaviour modification and sun-protective measures. Regular use of a good quality moisturising cream is also important. There are also three different topical treatments which can be used, although all three have the potential to irritate the skin during the active treatment phase.'

I reeled off the three treatments, and Allyson Brown explained in more detail how each should be applied. The GPs were listening intently, most of them apparently hearing this for the first time.

The discussion about the man with psoriasis enabled me to illustrate the impact of psoriasis on a patient's quality of life. Was his skin itchy, sore or uncomfortable? Did his psoriasis affect his choice of clothing to wear? Did his psoriasis impact on his work? Did his skin disease stop him from sleeping? Was his psoriasis affecting his love life?

The young woman with an odd-looking mole was also a good case to teach on. I explained about the importance of listening to the story. It is often the case that the clue to the diagnosis comes in the story, not necessarily in the appearance of the mole. I showed the GPs how to do dermoscopy, and allowed each of them to use my dermatoscope to examine the mole. This little device was a game-changer for dermatology; like using binoculars for the first time when bird watching. All of a sudden it was possible to appreciate a whole extra level of detail which was not possible with the naked eye. The GPs seemed to be impressed. I reassured the young woman that the mole appeared to be benign, and could safely be left alone. She seemed pleased, and went out with a smile.

The meeting was a success; another great group of GPs who were clearly operating at a high level; another positive reception for the integrated care model, with the GPs eager to take on more responsibility with our support. Most importantly, this was seven more GPs whom I had met, eaten lunch with and shared experiences and opinions about dermatology; we had concluded with shared learning through consultations involving their own patients. I wrote brief notes on the meeting in my diary, taking particular care to record the names of the GPs and the two nurses. In future interactions with each of these health care professionals I would use their first names.

The third meeting was in Blaenau Ffestiniog, a remote town located close to the old slate quarries overlooking Southern

Snowdonia, now a World Heritage Site. The wind-battered landscape had been extensively scarred by slate mining. I knew that the town had significant poverty and social problems. Nevertheless, I was looking forward to visiting Canolfan Goffa Ffestiniog, the newly refurbished community hospital which I had yet to visit; Blaenau Ffestiniog's GPs were located there in a health board-managed practice at the community hospital. Dr Otilia Azamfirei, one of our dermatology speciality doctors, joined me, her interest piqued by the positive buzz surrounding these meetings and our new model of care. Canolfan Goffa Ffestiniog lived up to expectations; the old stone exterior had been retained, keeping the charm of the original building which had been created and paid for by the local slate-miners. Inside was a brand-new building, well-designed and modern.

'None of us have any experience in dermatology,' was the first thing the group of GPs told us.

Next came questions about skin cancer: GPs in Holland do much more skin minor surgery than was the norm for GPs in the UK, one GP mentioned. Unfortunately, NICE guidance had given the GPs a more marginal role in the surgical management of skin cancer. There was a question about skin photography, with the GP explaining the practical issues around sending clinical photos with referral letters. These were all salaried GPs, employed by the health board, which took overall responsibility for employing the staff and running the practice. Some of them also did sessions in other GP surgeries. I was trying to keep up, and remember these complex arrangements. There were no patients this time, but we made up for it with a series of detailed case discussions about their patients.

Innovation and service change had brought us together; the teaching of Clayton Christensen and the passion of Don Berwick meant that we were able to remove barriers (real or imagined) between the generalist and specialist teams, just as William Osler had removed barriers between himself and his students and between himself and his patients. Through these meetings we all gained insight into the health care environments within which we were operating, just as Don Berwick demonstrated in his collected speeches to the Institute for Healthcare Improvement. Here, Berwick describes how his wife and he experienced the course of her recent serious illness:

'Instead of patient-centred care, we found ourselves enmeshed in onerous rules and assaults on our dignity, and we found our caregivers too often interested in explaining how something must be done instead of asking us how we needed it to be done. We felt forgotten. Instead of a smoothly flowing and constantly coordinated system – instead of a system at all - we found that we were sailing from medical island to medical island, carrying incomplete messages to institutions and people who never seemed to understand that they were part of a whole.'

This short paragraph from Berwick resonated with my own clinical practice in North Wales twenty years later. By coming together with colleagues in primary care, we were trying to create a whole system that worked for our patients in an integrated and joined-up way. The appeal of Dermatology Integrated Care was its success in using our NHS, both staff and resources, to provide a service that was free at the point of delivery. When the NHS works, there's no need for private practice as an escape valve. With Dermatology Integrated Care, patients were given the standard of care that Bevan and Lloyd-George would have wanted. Why was Dermatology Integrated Care such a success? Because at its core it was about establishing human interaction where none existed previously; the specialist and generalist teams coming together, for the common good, to improve patient care.

As we chatted together, I was struck by the novelty of seeing GPs and dermatology specialists listening with interest and sympathy to each other's stories of working in the NHS, just as Archie Cochrane and Julian Tudor Hart had done with each other as Cochrane was preparing to write his book *Effectiveness and Efficiency: Random Reflections on Health Services* and Tudor Hart was developing his ideas in anticipation of creating the inverse care law. I also thought of Betsi Cadwaladr in the kitchens of the hospital at Balaclava in the Crimean War, and how she had galvanised her small team and used their limited resources to transform healthcare for the sick and wounded soldiers. How interesting to note that we have it within our power to make a difference, and to transform healthcare, if we chose to do so. These examples are related by a determination for their protagonists to apply common sense, best practice and to create a system of care where social justice prevails.

•   •   •

FEMALE, SEVENTY-THREE, BAD ECZEMA

She is seventy-three and has late-onset eczema with terribly itchy skin. It had come on suddenly about eighteen months earlier. The creams aren't working and she feels ugly and unattractive; the itching is stopping her from sleeping.

'How about ultraviolet light therapy?' I suggest. 'It's often very effective for eczema.'

We discuss the logistics. 'Three times per week for up to ten weeks.'

'I can't,' she says. 'That's too much. Our son is special needs. He's thirty-seven and lives independently. My husband and I take it in turns to look after him during the day.'

'What do you do with him?' I ask.

'Just three things: cinema, trainspotting and swimming.'

'What's his name?' I ask.

'William,' she says, apparently surprised that I have asked. She reaches into her handbag and pulls out her mobile phone. 'Here he is,' she says proudly, showing me her phone. 'Our lovely boy.'

'We can do phototherapy twice weekly if three times is too much.'

'Really? Yes, I think that might work.'

CHAPTER 26

THE TELEDERMATOLOGY TRANSFORMATION

2019-2020

I*'d get that mole checked if I were you.*

It's a friend who makes the comment.

The mole has been there for ages and has never caused you concern. Now it plays on your mind. What if it's skin cancer? You realise that you're being melodramatic. Calm down. It's probably nothing. You will ask your GP when you're next there.

A few weeks later: '…and doctor, while I'm here, would you mind also checking a mole? It's probably nothing, but I think it might have changed.'

Your GP takes a quick look and says, 'I'll refer you to a dermatologist, to be on the safe side. Just sit over there, and I will photograph it for the referral letter.'

Oh dear! It might be skin cancer. Anxiety levels start to build again. A few days later, you get a letter back from the hospital.

It's from the consultant dermatologist herself; a personalised letter, which is reassuring. She says it looks benign and does not need to be cut out. What a relief; so speedy, and no appointment at the hospital was needed.

The use of photographs to compliment GP referral letters to dermatologists started in the NHS about twenty years ago. It is now widespread, and since COVID-19 has become the norm for dermatology. This is termed 'teledermatology'. Teledermatology has transformed the way dermatologists work across the UK. Before we asked GPs to include photographs with their referrals, the dermatology clinics were full of patients being seen urgently, with stories similar to the scenario above. These patients were usually referred on the fast-track cancer pathway, to be seen within two weeks of receipt of referral letter. As a result, more severe and distressing skin diseases were pushed down the waiting list.

As there were no funds to invest in a bespoke teledermatology service, the system we introduced was pragmatic, requiring GPs to take the photographs themselves with their own cameras. For the first few months, non-urgent referral letters without photographs were returned to the GP with a polite letter explaining how photographs would improve patient care. We invoked Berwick and Osler by appealing to the GP's best instincts for excellent patient care: a photograph might avoid the need for a hospital appointment; a photograph might result in speedier patient access to specialist services such as plastic surgery; a photograph might lead to a direct booking for a surgical procedure, a 'one-stop-shop', saving the patient from extra appointments. Most GPs could see the sense in these arguments, and were persuaded without being mandated. We also gave technical advice on how to take clinical photos and directed GPs to use free apps that were compatible with General Medical Council guidance on doctors taking photos of patients.

From the GP perspective, a photograph sounds easy, but requires infrastructure and a system to make it happen. There are technical issues regarding the taking of the photo itself. Is the lighting correct? Is there a plain background? How many photos should be taken to show the appearance and distribution of the rash or skin lesion? There are also consent issues, as the photograph forms part of the patient medical record. There are time issues concerning when the photo is taken and by whom; not forgetting governance and regulatory issues concerning GPs using their own cameras to take medical photos. There are cyber-security issues concerning sending images with the referral letter; and more technical issues in loading the photo onto the system, attaching it to the referral letter and sending the two together.

Despite this, it worked. The rate of GP referrals with photographs steadily increased from 20 per cent to 90 per cent in a six-month period. Furthermore, most of the photographs were of decent quality. With no extra funding, we had created a new referral system which allowed us to prioritise patient referrals in a new and more carefully considered way. I was reminded of Christensen; what exactly was the job that our patients needed us to do?

Patients who were focused on a changing skin lesion just wanted timely reassurance from an expert who knew what they were talking about. This advice needed to be personal, rapid, ideally avoiding an unnecessary hospital appointment. For example, the following patient, who described her experience by email to another member of my team (who then shared it with me): 'Got a letter from Prof. Anstey who discharged me from his waiting list. If you ever see him and he's interested, can you pass on my thank you for the reply? It's been really helpful.'

For patients with severe skin disease, disrupted sleep and a negative impact on their quality of life, an urgent referral meant a fast clinic appointment for face-to-face assessment and management plan. Importantly, urgent means urgent for these patients, not a wait of four months. The first patient I remember seeing within four weeks instead of the previous four months was a fourteen-year-old boy from Blaenau Ffestiniog who attended with his mother. Owain had severe, scarring acne on the face, chest and back. He responded rapidly to the treatment he was prescribed in the dermatology clinic. His smiling face a few weeks later was a fitting reward for our efforts to improve access to dermatology for patients like him. He was just one of many patients with bad skin disease who were now being seen within four weeks; I knew we were on the right track.

For elderly patients with a lesion requiring a skin biopsy or a simple surgical procedure, the job they were seeking to get done was a streamlined process to sort it out with as few visits to the hospital as possible; preferably one appointment rather than three. For patients with serious skin cancers, the job they were seeking to get done was to access the expert surgeon who would excise the cancer without delay. The photo-triage system works particularly well for these patients, the referral with photographs passing through the system without unnecessary stops en route and ending up with the right person. Furthermore, the photographs gave the surgeon an idea of what was coming their way before seeing the patient; the planning of care was already taking shape in their mind.

Finally, let us not forget that the routine referrals are also patients who want to get a job done. It may not be urgent, but it is still of importance to them. The job these patients want done is to receive a timely diagnosis, an explanation about the nature of the condition, an idea about the prognosis (the outlook) and natural history (in other words, what will happen if it is left untreated), and also a management plan. Our new teledermatology system allowed me to write advice and guidance letters to many of these patients. These individualised letters sent directly to the patient (the GP was copied in) sought to address the job that the patient was seeking to get done. I did hundreds of these letters over an eighteen-month period as I steadily worked my way through the routine waiting list. I was kept motivated by the monthly waiting list figures, which confirmed that this was working; month after month the routine waiting list was falling. Some of the patients wrote back to thank me, saying how helpful my letter had been. Hardly any patients complained, despite these letters ending with the following two sentences: 'I hope this letter has been helpful to you. We will not be sending you an appointment for the dermatology clinic.'

This new way of working was an asset during the COVID-19 crisis; we already had a system and infrastructure which permitted teledermatology consultations with patients instead of face-to-face appointments at the hospital. It was just a matter of increasing from 20–25 per cent of referrals being dealt with in this way, to 90–95 per cent of referrals. We also decided to reply directly to the GP referrals within a day or two of receipt of new referral letters. In most cases it was possible to create constructive responses to the GPs, which they could use to manage that patient in the community. For the GPs, this was a novelty: no sooner had they referred a case to the hospital for an opinion than that opinion was forthcoming. Importantly, patients were being dealt with quickly, and work at the hospital was not building up.

Our system for teledermatology was flawed; it permitted clinical photographs to be sent with referral letters whilst having none of the safeguards and ease of use of a bespoke, modern, purpose-built teledermatology system. This was effectively a prototype system. Design thinking teaches us that prototyping is a legitimate and sensible way to initiate change by making our ideas tangible. Tim Brown, an expert on design thinking, advises, 'The faster we make our ideas tangible, the sooner we will be able to evaluate them, refine them, and zero in on the best solution.' We had created a prototype teledermatology system by using the existing system differently. This had the advantage of being available without delay, and costing nothing. However, lack of encryption for these images meant that it was not as secure as needed. The prototype had served its purpose by proving the case for this novel way of working. Our collective experience gleaned over the previous twelve months had confirmed that teledermatology must be central to our change process. We now needed something much better. The solution was surprisingly simple: two apps were available to doctors for taking photos with their own cameras; both were free and easy to use. Importantly, both apps were also compliant with guidance from the General Medical Council to doctors on use of their own phones for taking patient images. All we needed to do was raise awareness about these apps with our local GPs and encourage and support them in their use.

A teledermatology system is only as good as the specialists who are responding to the GP referrals. This was brought home to me after my two-week summer holiday when I found myself facing a backlog of GP referrals which had not been dealt with. The less experienced dermatologists in my team had found the experience too challenging at their stage of training. This prompted a rethink about the skills required for success in teledermatology; teaching these skills would be an essential element when training junior dermatologists. My experience of responding to the referrals accompanied by photographs confirmed that success required speed, as the volume of referrals was so high: twenty to forty new cases daily in our area. Speed in medicine usually requires the use of heuristics, or rules of thumb. These are the reflex, mental shortcuts that bypass any analytical process, promoting rapid solutions to a problem. This was why the less experienced dermatologists in my team left in charge when I was on holiday were unable to cope. I had more than thirty years of experience to draw on; these mental shortcuts were already an established part of my work. In contrast, my two colleagues were much less experienced. The alternative to heuristics is a slow, reflective process involving analytic effort. My junior colleagues did not possess tried and tested heuristics in their dermatology toolboxes; they were unable to process teledermatology referrals in a timely way as they were thinking long and hard about each case. As the workload accumulated, panic had set in, and their responses had ended up being done in haste. Of course, haste is quite different to heuristics; the only thing they share is speediness. In contrast to heuristics, haste leads to errors and omissions, and has no place in medicine. However, too much heuristics can also lead to mistakes; not everything in medicine is straightforward and easy. Thus, our responses to these GP referrals required us to use a slower, more reflective approach for selected cases. It was like doing a multiple-choice examination: some questions could be answered quickly, whilst some required more thought to work out the right answer.

Dermatology Integrated Care provided us with the opportunity to meet with, and get to know, the extended primary care team. We were now using our knowledge of the GP or nurse who had sent the referral to tailor our replies, aiming always for the highest chance of success. Thus, responses to GP trainees, practice nurses, physician associates, locum GPs, salaried GPs, GP partners, foundation year GPs, and GPs with a special interest in dermatology or skin surgery were all slightly different, according to the health care professional. This was the strength of our system, which was not one-size fits all. The response by GPs to these carefully crafted advice and guidance emails was overwhelmingly positive. The nuances and subtleties of the interactions allowed us to reinforce our service model of integration; we were all on the same side, working towards a common goal. The acid test that would determine the success or otherwise of Dermatology Integrated Care was whether it worked in practice, with patients flowing smoothly along referral pathways and being seen in a timely fashion. If the patient flow was sorted out, there was a great chance of success.

* * *

FEMALE, FIFTY-SIX, RASH ON FACE

Fifty-six, purple hair, and matching purple glasses with decorative frames in the style of, but less exuberant than, Dame Edna. She has a rash on her face. It had started with a couple of spots on her chin. Self-medication with hydrocortisone cream from the bathroom cabinet. It had worked. A few days later, the rash had come back, slightly worse than before. She saw her GP, explaining that hydrocortisone cream had initially worked. Next, a stronger steroid cream. It also had worked, but then the rash had come back again; now it was more extensive, extending around the mouth onto the upper lip.

I listen to the story and examine the skin.

'What is it?' she asks.

'Steroid-provoked rosacea, sometimes called perioral dermatitis,' I reply. She looks surprised. It dawns on her that she has caused this herself.

I advise her to avoid steroid creams to the face, and to take a once daily tetracycline tablet for twelve weeks. 'It should all settle down by then,' was my confident prediction. I also jot down the website for the British Association of Dermatologists so she can read more about this condition.

CHAPTER 27

PATIENT FLOW

1965-2019

Every six months the dermatologists in Wales meet up for a half day; the agenda includes discussion about dermatology clinical services across the principality. The chairperson goes around the room, asking dermatologists from each health board to report on their service. I have attended these meetings for nearly thirty years; this part of the meeting is an unchanging ritual, each centre reporting the same thing: long waiting lists. Furthermore, these long waiting lists are usually linked to the need to recruit more consultants; a standard solution, 'We need more staff.' The responsibility for these waiting lists is pinned firmly on 'management' by the assembled dermatologists; there are no managers present at these meetings, so there's no danger of being contradicted in this opinion. Blaming managers for our woes is briefly cathartic, our collective determination to recruit more staff perhaps easing any sense of guilt we might feel about our thriving private practices. But this assessment is overly simplistic and fails to capture the complexity and nuances of running an NHS clinical service. Importantly, no one gains if we seek to blame others for the poor performance of our services. Furthermore, there is no chance of improving the service for those who adopt this negative philosophy.

Dermatology is relatively sheltered from discussions about patient flow in NHS hospitals, being predominantly an outpatient discipline. There are now courses on patient flow, books on patient flow, and experts on the topic, none more so than Don Berwick and the Institute for Healthcare Improvement. Patient flow is one of Berwick's defining principles of good healthcare; it is part of his mantra. Berwick believes that optimising patient flow is everyone's job in clinical medicine; the flip side of this is that flow failure leading to long waiting lists is everyone's responsibility. I would go further than this: long waiting lists in dermatology result in significant levels of misery for our patients; the more waiting, the greater the misery. Berwick tells us that durable improvement in patient flow is not an accident; it takes great effort.

What do we mean by patient flow? The basics of patient flow start with five recommendations from the Institute for Healthcare Improvement white paper on the topic. All five of these points are relevant to the delivery of outpatient dermatology services in the modern NHS.

POINT ONE

Make delivery of the right care, in the right place, at the right time a strategic priority

For dermatology this concerns the process used for allocating patients to different clinical pathways and the need to ensure that each of these pathways is carefully constructed to ensure maximum efficiency.

As a young child I watched *Play School*, a BBC children's TV programme in the 1960s. A highlight of *Play School* was the journey through the windows: there were three, one arched, one round and one square. The programme presenter would pose the question, 'Which window are we going through today, children?' After a brief pause, the camera would zoom in on one window, and the journey would begin. Many NHS dermatology departments, including my own until January 2019, have a process for allocating referrals to clinical pathways which is equal in sophistication to the *Play School* windows of the 1960s: there are just three choices. Which one will it be? Perhaps urgent suspected cancer? Or urgent? Or routine? With just three options, it is not possible to select one that suits every referral. Will these three categories ensure delivery of the right care, in the right place, at the right time? Or will they lead to waste, with patients seeing the wrong person, in the wrong place, at the wrong time?

POINT TWO

Align staff and hospital executives
to achieve improved flow

The bottom line is that the executives need to get out and interact with clinical teams. Both management and clinical teams must understand that excellence in patient flow is a priority for the organisation. For dermatology, this involves looking at the whole service and understanding the dynamics of the system. Doing more clinics, or recruiting more staff, is unlikely to have a lasting impact on patient flow; at best, this achieves a temporary shortening of waiting lists. However, a clear understanding of the dynamics of patient flow for each speciality can lead to discussion by the team on how to improve the whole system performance. Appointing more consultants is rarely the solution. The reason for this is the relationship between the small specialist team and the large number of local GPs. Appointing more consultants does not alter this dynamic; with a new recruit, the consultant team is still small and easily swamped by a tiny change in referral patterns by each member of the large pool of GPs. It's like trying to dig a hole in a desert (with the grains of sand representing patients and the people doing the digging being the consultants); after initial progress, the hole remains the same size, with as much sand running back in as the diggers throw out. Two diggers instead of one does not significantly alter this dynamic.

POINT THREE

Adopt value-based care models to support improved flow

Make sure that each step in a clinical pathway has value for the patient. Rather than appoint more consultants, specialist teams should focus on creating value-based care models by collaborating closely with that huge resource in the community: our GP colleagues. After all, most dermatology in the NHS is done by GPs, not by dermatologists.

POINT FOUR

**Demonstrate that improved patient flow
has a positive return on investment**

For Dermatology Integrated Care, the executives needed no convincing: our service had the best patient flow, the shortest waiting lists, and was the least expensive model of care for dermatology in the health board.

POINT FIVE

**Connect the work of all departments and
units to hospital-wide flow strategies**

In other words, implementing and sustaining improvements in patient flow across healthcare organisations requires alignment, cooperation and coordination. Put simply, improvement will only be sustained if everyone joins in. Those specialities and departments that are doing well must share their success with those who aspire to do better.

The new way of working championed by Dermatology Integrated Care was more complex, with a radically changed pattern of work. Clinical care now included office-based activity in front of a computer screen, where previously almost all clinical care was face-to-face with patients in clinic. In contrast to the old way of working, there were now nine entry points for GP patient referrals:

1. Urgent suspected cancer
2. Urgent referral
3. Routine referral
4. Fast track phototherapy
5. Email response to GP referral within forty-eight hours with advice and guidance
6. Typed advice and guidance letters to patients (copies to GP) within two weeks of referral
7. Direct to skin surgery (one-stop service)
8. Nurse-led service
9. Referral onwards to plastic surgery or maxillofacial surgery

Pathway one: urgent suspected cancer

These referrals were now more appropriate, with benign-looking lesions sifted out during the referral process, and barn-door melanomas and squamous cell carcinomas fast-tracked to surgery or to other members of the skin cancer multidisciplinary team via pathway nine.

Pathway two: urgent referrals

These referrals included conditions such as severe acne, severe eczema, severe psoriasis and any skin disorder which was having a big impact on the patient's life. In the new system there was no waiting list for urgent referrals, all of whom were seen within four weeks. This was the greatest triumph of Dermatology Integrate Care; urgent referrals seen urgently.

Pathway three: routine referrals

Many referrals previously seen in clinic after months of waiting were now dealt with by advice and guidance letters to the patient and GP. The reduced need for clinic appointments led to a steady fall in the waiting list for routine face-to-face clinic appointments.

Pathway four: Fast track for phototherapy

This pathway was created in recognition of the long wait patients were experiencing for ultraviolet light therapy. The old way required a GP referral requesting repeat phototherapy; the referral letter was typically prioritised as routine. The patient then waited for up to fourteen months to be seen in clinic. Four weeks later the patient started treatment, fifteen months after the original referral. In the new system the response to the GP was via the phototherapy fast track. Patients were invited to phone to book an appointment at a time and date that was convenient for them. Four weeks after receipt of referral they started phototherapy.

Pathway five: rapid email response to GP referral
This was created during the COVID-19 lockdown; the imperative was to avoid hospital appointments wherever possible. Referrals during the crisis generated an email response from the specialist team to the GP within forty-eight hours. This consisted of a carefully written advice and guidance letter.

Pathway six: Advice and guidance letters to patients
These personalised letters sent directly to patients impacted significantly on the overall performance of Dermatology Integrated Care. How so? Because these patients were previously waiting to be seen at the hospital and the hospital outpatient department represented a bottleneck. We had limited capacity, determined by the number of doctors and nurses in the team, the number of outpatient rooms available, space and capacity of the waiting area, and the number of nurses available to support us. By dealing with patient referrals differently, we were removing significant numbers of patients who would otherwise have required face-to-face appointments.

Pathway seven: direct to skin surgery
Better known in the NHS as a 'one-stop shop', direct to surgery was common sense. Most patients requiring skin surgery were elderly; many lived far from the hospital and depended on family and friends to help them to attend. If we could sort them out with one appointment rather than three, so much the better. Again, this service did the job that each of us needed doing: the elderly patient had just one appointment, not three.

Pathway eight: nurse-led care

Contemporary medicine is delivered by teams of clinicians including specialist nurses. Each of our three nurse specialists was resourceful and unique. All three were nurse prescribers, able to prescribe drugs routinely used in dermatology in the same way as the doctors in our team. By changing the nurses to front-line staff, dermatology teams create much needed additional capacity. Our nurses were particularly good at providing protocol-driven clinical services, being efficient and conscientious with excellent interpersonal skills. Many patient referrals from GPs could now be allocated straight to the nurses via clinical pathway eight.

Pathway nine: referral onwards to plastic surgery or maxillofacial surgery

All referrals from GPs of skin lesions now included clinical photographs. Those needing a specialist surgeon were triaged directly to the appropriate surgical team. In addition to making the pathway faster, this also avoided unneeded clinic appointments with dermatology.

Nine new clinical pathways, carefully constructed to optimise the use of our limited resources, and provide speedy access to care for those who most needed it. But did it work?

●　　●　　●

GIRL, SIXTEEN, BAD ACNE

Elin had been on oral antibiotics for her acne on and off since the age of twelve. Her GP had recently added the contraceptive pill as treatment for her acne, but it had not worked. She was becoming increasingly despondent, and reluctant to go out or go to school. Her GP mentioned that the hospital might be able to help and suggested referral to dermatology. Elin was warned to expect a long wait (Dermatology Integrated Care had only recently been introduced; GPs were unfamiliar with the short waiting times). Photographs of Elin's acne were included with the referral letter; four weeks later, she was seen in my clinic. I explained to Elin and her mother that she required treatment with isotretinoin, a strong but very effective treatment for severe acne.

Four months later, her skin is much improved. More importantly, so is her mood and her outward expression. Elin's mum is delighted, as she has reverted to the vivacious and outgoing teenager whom she knows and loves.

CHAPTER 28

DERMATOLOGY INTEGRATED CARE BEDS IN

2019-2020

I was nervous that the waiting lists would remain stuck despite our best efforts.

When Dermatology Integrated Care was introduced, I'd hoped to see the waiting lists falling *every month*. Informatics, the NHS department dedicated to monitoring the NHS performance data, was asked to help. I was emailed a link with access to the dermatology performance figures for the whole health board, called the 'dermatology dashboard', like the dashboard of a car, generating data which permitted detailed assessment of our performance. There was so much data, much of it unfamiliar to me.

We were advised to give it a month. One month later there it was. I felt a strong sense of relief – both the routine and urgent waiting lists showed a small but sharp downturn, quite different to the usual activity over previous months. Something was happening, but not enough to prove a point. I would need to be patient. Month two passed: I clicked on the link and went straight to the waiting list graphs. Again, both urgent and routine waiting lists continued to show a sharp downturn, now longer and more sustained. So, all of the performance data was now moving in the same direction, from dismal to bad, through not-too-bad, heading towards reasonable; in the far distance I could imagine good, and then excellent. By month six it was clear to me that the new way of working was succeeding; I needed to start sharing this with colleagues. I talked it through with the lead GP in our area and my partner in changing the service; we agreed to write it up as a short document to be shared.

The dermatology dashboard continued to provide data on all aspects of our performance, including the waiting lists. This data was plotted graphically month on month. It showed the new areas of activity which had contributed to these dramatic improvements in our waiting lists: the number of advice and guidance letters; the number of direct referrals onwards to other disciplines without the need for a dermatology appointment; the number of one-stop minor surgery appointments. Many patients no longer needed to be seen in the dermatology clinic, opening up more slots for patients on the waiting lists. The waiting list for urgent referrals disappeared altogether within nine months of introducing Dermatology Integrated Care; patients now booked with a clinic appointment within three to four weeks

With a reduced demand for face-to-face clinic appointments, it was now possible to offer patients more choice, including the option of evening dermatology clinics. I was struck by the change in atmosphere between evening clinics and daytime clinics. It was the same patients and the same staff in the same clinic rooms, but at a different time; so why the change in atmosphere? The answer was threefold: parking, the patient's jobs and a calm environment. The hospital car parks empty rapidly after five; evening appointments seldom require time off work for patients; there were no competing clinics, so the outpatient department was quiet and peaceful. This is another striking example of healthcare delivering on the job that the patient is seeking to get done, exactly as Christensen had urged us to consider. If the patient were to list their requirements, this clinic ticked most of the boxes. Why does this matter? Because having unstressed patients attending at a time that suits them usually results in improved interactions with the clinic staff. Doctoring becomes more enjoyable if the patients are relaxed and mentally ready for the forthcoming interaction. If patients ask the right questions and are listened to, they have a good chance of creating a shared agenda with their dermatologist. This in turn improves the chance of better patient outcomes and greater patient adherence.

The disappearing NHS waiting lists presented a unique opportunity to consider their effect on those with a stake in the service: our patients; the GPs; the clinical team; the clerical and administration team; our managers. The waiting list data was certainly attention-grabbing and dramatic, but how did it affect each of us at a personal level?

By now it was evident that patients were benefiting from Dermatology Integrated Care: fast access for urgent referrals, prompt responses with advice and guidance letters, and one-stop surgery were all popular. However, the most popular feature was the end to long waiting lists. Kerrie Gallear, our dermatology clinic clerk, used to send patients a letter confirming receipt of the GP referral, and warning that the wait for an appointment would be twenty-six weeks or more. For many patients it was receipt of this letter which led to their request for a private referral. Kerrie no longer sends this letter. Furthermore, GPs told me that patients now seldom requested referral to the private sector.

The feedback from the trainee dermatologists was also positive. They were proud to be part of this change process which was impacting so positively on patient care, and told me that the changes that we had introduced were long overdue. They greatly enjoyed the opportunity to participate in the new teledermatology service; we worked together as a team to develop and refine the way we responded to the GP referrals. They joined me on the visits to meet up with the GPs in their own surgeries. There were three highlights for the dermatology trainees of being so closely involved in this change process. Firstly, they rapidly gained experience in teledermatology, which had emerged as the single most important service change in dermatology for decades. This was an area where all dermatologists needed to become expert and highly competent; our trainees were ahead of the curve. Secondly, the trainees were proud that our teledermatology service was singled out for praise at a national training day in London that they were attending. Thirdly, they were delighted to be part of our departmental application for the BMJ Dermatology Team of the Year award, and proud that our entry made it to the final four teams in the UK.

The problems with long dermatology waiting lists elsewhere in the health board were taking place adjacent to our patch, where everything was improving without new investment or extra staff. From their point of view, our team's performance was counterintuitive and made no sense. They were vocal with their criticisms and made it clear to the dermatology managers their intention to stick with their model of care. This must have been a galling for them; similar to the experience of the England football team in 1953, beaten 3:6 by Hungary at Wembley in the 'Match of the Century'. Except that the England football team retained their dignity and professionalism, with no tirades against the Hungarians, who were worthy victors; they channelled the pain of this experience into a process of change. Training and tactics were improved, creating a new trajectory; England won the World Cup in 1966.

All three of the dermatology specialist nurses were positive about Dermatology Integrated Care. 'It has meant that the dermatology service has become much leaner,' Rhian explained. 'Patients who really need a face-to-face consultation with the dermatology team no longer wait long. Patients are seen much sooner, with urgent cases seen within days or a couple of weeks rather than months.'

Alison Kemp, a dermatology operational manager, was amazed by the impact of Dermatology Integrated Care. All three of the dermatology operational managers expected the service in West to just avoid breaching the NHS deadlines. However, from April 2019, something more dramatic had started to occur: the dermatology waiting lists in West had started to tumble down. The dermatology managers were excited to discuss this at their regular dermatology service review meetings. What was happening in West to explain this unexpected and unprecedented service improvement? Alison had no recollection of money being allocated for waiting list initiatives (extra clinics to reduce waiting lists). In Alison's experience, this was the only way to shift recalcitrant waiting lists. All eyes were on Eleri Roberts, the operational manager for dermatology in West, who allowed a subtle smile to play across her face.

'What's going on, Eleri?' Alison asked in her usual direct manner.

'We have changed our system,' Eleri replied, trying her best not to sound smug. She then told them about Dermatology Integrated Care. The managers already knew that the service in West had used unspent consultant salaries to appoint more nurses and GPs to the team. This had happened a couple of years earlier, initially with no apparent benefit to the service. Training and sign-off as a nurse prescriber takes time and had only recently been completed. Similarly for the GPs; it had taken months for them to be trained, but all four GPs were now devoted to dermatology, and had become valued members of the team.

'Your team's productivity is quite remarkable,' acknowledged Alison wistfully, as she looked at the informatics dashboard for dermatology; it was the same health board, the same GPs, the same patients, yet one part of the health board had a steadily falling waiting list, whilst the rest of dermatology in the health board had waiting lists that were heading in the opposite direction. Eleri clarified this for her fellow dermatology managers:

'In case you were wondering, there is no extra cash in our system and no new recruits to explain this performance. We are just using our resources differently.'

Alison was stunned and rather envious; this was an example of innovation and service change in her own health board, happening in an under-resourced service led by a single consultant with a team of nurses and GPs. Framing this service change as integrated care effectively placed dermatology services in the community as part of primary care. Here was an opportunity for dermatology to forge links with primary care, which was exactly what was happening. Like all great ideas, it made sense and was easy to understand; Alison was a convert.

* * *

MALE, TWENTY-ONE, BAD ECZEMA

He works at a well-known out-of-town warehouse store selling training shoes and sports kit. As his skin was so bad and everyone knows NHS waiting lists are long, his mum suggested he should see a dermatologist privately, and she would pay. He went to see his GP to request a private referral. No need, said his GP. Two weeks later Jake is seen by us. Jake tells me his story; his eyes filled with tears. Although his skin is bad, the solutions are straightforward. In two weeks' time his skin will be much better; he is now on the path to recovery.

CHAPTER 29

A SUCCESSFUL DISRUPTION?

1890–2021

William Osler's style of practicing medicine was certainly new. When he burst upon the North American medical scene at the end of the nineteenth century, this new approach, alongside his commitment to scholarship and a charismatic personality, ensured that his rise to the top was rapid and sustained. His view that medicine needed to be more science-based, and his humanistic approach to patient interaction resonated with doctors and patients around the world. Out went paternalistic, anecdotal medicine, and in came something which had greater value for all concerned. Doctors who listened carefully to their patients; who were experts in medical science; who were caring, kind and sympathetic; doctors filled with empathy and insight; doctors who aspired to and cherished professionalism; who kept up to date with advances in medicine and shared their knowledge by teaching others. His innovative approach meant that doctors were able to embrace a more humanistic and patient-centred approach to medical care to the benefit of everyone.

Equally innovative was Archie Cochrane who, frustrated by the inconsistencies he observed in healthcare, realised the need for proper evidence to demonstrate effectiveness and efficacy of treatments. This approach had huge value as it sought to identify and eradicate treatments that did not work. Cochrane quotes Osler in his famous book *Effectiveness and Efficiency*: 'A desire to take medicine is perhaps the great feature that distinguishes man from other animals.' Cochrane's view, when his book came out, was that 'one should be delightfully surprised when any treatment at all is effective, and always assume that a treatment is ineffective unless there is evidence to the contrary.' Cochrane went on to provide a hierarchy for evidence for treatments, from the lowest level (level six), where randomised controlled trials do not exist, but could be designed and applied, to level one for treatments that are justified by their immediate and obvious effect, such as insulin for diabetes. He highlighted, for example, that no evidence existed to justify tonsillectomy, a surgical procedure widely practiced in the 1950s and 1960s, but now largely abandoned. He also highlighted the wide variation in hospital length of stay, ranging from day surgery for hernias as an outpatient, to a lengthy stay in hospital for the same procedure. We had exactly the same debate for inpatient care in dermatology as recently as ten years ago, with some dermatologists insisting that inpatient care was both necessary and desirable, whilst most dermatology centres had already stopped this practice. By shifting the focus to ensure that clinicians were more thoughtful and discriminating about treatments, Cochrane saved the NHS precious resources by highlighting those that did work. Out went anecdotal therapies and practices, in came evidence-based medicine. The innovation that followed, the Cochrane Library, created a process for sifting the evidence in a systematic way, in the form of a systematic review.

Don Berwick was interested in the detail of how health service systems function. His insights related to patient flow, the need to collaborate and work with each other, and the need to eliminate waste from healthcare. As a philosophy and guiding principle, Berwick's approach cannot be faulted. Furthermore, it was true innovation; by reducing waste his approach to patient flow saved money and improved the value of healthcare. By highlighting the need for smooth patient flow along value-enhanced clinical pathways, Berwick was improving patient access by making healthcare more efficient.

A useful guide to assess if change to a service is truly innovative is to see how rapidly the old model is jettisoned once the new model of care becomes established. Additionally, the best innovative ideas are rapidly adopted by others as the shortcomings of the original model become apparent. It was only when the scale of service improvement generated by Dermatology Integrated Care become apparent that it occurred to me that we might have, inadvertently, created a form of innovation as described by Christensen in his book *The Innovator's Prescription*. However, this was not our intention at the outset.

It was Christensen who observed that, 'the disruptive innovation theory explains the process by which complicated, expensive products and services are transformed into simple and affordable ones. It also shows why it is so difficult for the leading companies or institutions in an industry to succeed at disruption. Historically, it is almost always new companies or totally independent business units of existing firms that succeed in disrupting industries.'

My team in North Wales operated separately and independently to the two other dermatology teams in our health board, yet we were all part of the same organisation. For the definition of disruptive innovation described above, my team represented 'a totally independent business unit', working within the same organisation. Christensen made an additional important observation: 'Business model innovations are almost always forged by new entrants to an industry.' Despite the fact that I had worked in dermatology for over thirty years, and was clearly not a new entrant into this particular industry, I *was* a new entrant into dermatology in North Wales. This was another box ticked for Christensen's definition of the process of disruptive innovation.

I was therefore interested to see if Dermatology Integrated Care fitted with the three specific criteria for disruptive innovation that Christensen had defined in his book: the technological enabler; business model innovation; and the value network.

The first of Christensen's three elements of innovation is a technological enabler. Christensen emphasised that the technological enablers of innovation are deployed initially against the industry's simplest problems. In our integrated care model, the technological enabler was digital photographs to accompany GP referral letters, not in itself a novel idea, but nevertheless a good one. Clear images shared between GPs and specialists transformed the level of interaction, like anaesthetics had transformed clinical practice for surgeons more than a century earlier. Initially, our focus was on photographs of skin lesions; these were the simplest problems, and represented the biggest chunk of our clinical workload, perhaps 60 per cent of the total.

What was simple about skin lesions? It was basically a binary choice: was this lesion benign or was it skin cancer? The presence of photographs with the referral letter allowed us to address the basic problems that GPs were faced with, in a low-cost way and with less human resource than was historically needed to do the same job in the clinic. Handheld digital cameras in smartphones are now ubiquitous in our society, and user experience is such that most photos we receive are high quality. We were taking advantage of technology that was freely available to local GPs.

This brings us to the second of Christensen's three elements of disruptive innovation: business model innovation. Christensen tells us that business model innovation requires that the new model is more affordable and more accessible than the previous model. For Dermatology Integrated Care the size and cost of the team required to deliver dermatology services was much smaller than the size and cost of the two other teams delivering the same service in the same health board in the same part of the NHS. The Dermatology Integrated Care business model was about delivering care that was more accessible to patients with much shorter waiting lists, whilst being significantly cheaper than the traditional models of care.

This leaves just one more of Christensen's elements for us to consider: the value network. Christensen describes the third enabler of disruption as the coalescence of an independent value network around the new business model through which care is delivered. What does this mean in practice? In the case of Dermatology Integrated Care, there were three separate and distinct networks which came together to make the new business model a success: NHS management; the specialist dermatology team; local teams of GPs. All three networks are capable of adopting opposing positions on any new proposed model of care.

Indeed, conflict and disagreement are more common between these three groups than harmony and agreement. This raises the question, why was there coalescence of the value network around Dermatology Integrated Care? It is difficult to be sure, but probably reflects the groundwork done by these three invested groups over previous months and years. NHS healthcare management in our area was high quality, with a reputation for working closely and harmoniously with the GPs and specialist consultant teams. Add into the mix a consultant who had trained as a GP, a service that was failing badly, an acute shortage of staff, and the old way of working having no supporters, and the case for coalescence of three independent value networks around the new business model was compelling for all parties.

* * *

When writing this book, I could think of just two other examples of a dermatology services for NHS patients which were operating with short waiting lists: The Sussex Community Dermatology Service and Cotswold Surgical Partners.

Sussex Community Dermatology Service was set up by a group of entrepreneurial consultant dermatologists led by Dr Russell Emerson. It was a service designed to compete directly with a local hospital-based NHS dermatology service. As with the Dermatology Integrated Care service in Bangor, the focus and emphasis of their business model was to provide services outside the traditional hospital-based service. This business model recognised that much of dermatology service provision did not require a hospital, and that hospital-based services were inherently costly. They offered consultant-led services, short waiting lists (no more than a six-week wait across all of their multiple clinic locations), a one-stop service for skin cancer management in over 80 per cent of patients, and care which was close to patients' homes. Their service had three techno-logical enablers: first, a clear and easy-to-use online referral system; second, an online teledermatology service; and third, highly efficient and up-to-date information technology systems. All three of these technologies probably outperformed the local hospital-based NHS dermatology service, placing the traditional NHS service on the back foot from the outset when competing for contracts. This was a truly innovative business model; their success spoke for itself. Russell told me they had started with a small team of three pioneering consultant dermatologists; over ten years it had grown to seventeen consultant dermatologists, three part-time maxillofacial surgeons and two part-time plastic surgeons. They were dealing with 40,000 new patient referrals per year, and with more than 100,000 patient contacts per year. It was a huge and impressive enterprise, and their data showed performance at the very top of the quality spectrum.

The philosophy for Cotswold Surgical Partners was to be collaborative with existing NHS dermatology providers. Despite this, dermatology colleagues did not always welcome them with open arms, tending to behave defensively at the outset and to be suspicious; one dermatologist described their arrival as 'your tanks parked on our front lawn'. Tom Millard, a dermatologist, has two colleagues in this business, both plastic surgeons. He described how they always under-promised and over-delivered for NHS contracts. I suggested that this sounded like a classic Trojan Horse; he smiled, not denying it. The business had been running for ten years, during which time they had built strong relationships with dermatologists, GPs and healthcare commissioners in the area. In other words, they had overcome the initial hostility.

What about the three elements Christensen had described as needing to be fulfilled for disruptive innovation? The technological enabler was that Cotswold Surgical Partners were using the same IT and systems as the NHS, but with a superfast connection, the latest computer hardware, and a full complement of staff. Importantly, the working environment was more like an investment bank than NHS administration facilities, making recruitment and retention of staff easier. I could see that the clerical side of this modern up-to-date facility was likely to outperform any rival hospital-based service administration system, giving them the edge. Secondly, their business model used the standard NHS tariff system, but with a cheaper cost base (the costs of premises in a modern business park being lower than the high overheads of a hospital setting). Thus, they would be profitable as a provider of NHS healthcare within this business model, whilst their colleagues in the local dermatology units would continue to be cash-strapped, and slow to initiate change. Finally, there was the value network. As with Sussex, so for the Cotswold Surgical Partners: it was hard for the local NHS service to compete. Their service was faster, better and cheaper. Importantly, at the core of this enterprise was a commitment to outstanding patient care. Thus, their value network had the coalescing interests of the commissioners, the local GPs, the patients, and even the local dermatologists.

The feature that differentiates the Bangor Dermatology Integrated Care service change from these other two models of innovation is that the Bangor innovation took advantage of an independent business unit within the NHS; the two other examples were independent companies which had disrupted local NHS services from the outside.

What do these three models of innovation in dermatology have in common? Firstly, all three were attuned to the need to be patient-focused. For both the Sussex Community Dermatology service and Cotswold Surgical Partners, this manifests as high levels of patient satisfaction, combined with fast turnaround times and short waiting lists; no wonder these entrepreneurs succeeded. For Dermatology Integrated Care, the emphasis was to create an efficient service, so that appointments were timely, and waiting lists reduced. GP satisfaction with Dermatology Integrated Care was high, and GPs reported that patient satisfaction was also high. Secondly, all three services were significantly cheaper than standard dermatology services. This financial undercutting allowed Sussex Community Dermatology and Cotswold Surgical Partners to gain a foothold as a local NHS service provider. For Dermatology Integrated Care, it was more a case of providing high quality services within a fixed budget, creating a cost per case which was significantly lower than the other two dermatology services in the same health board. Thirdly, all three models of care focused strongly on the issue of convenience and accessibility of the clinical service, with their main focus being the creation of novel and effective dermatology services in the community. The Sussex Community Dermatology service runs clinics from fifteen different venues scattered throughout their catchment area; this makes it much more likely that services will be available close to where patients live. Cotswold Surgical Partners are conveniently located close to a main motorway junction, and offer free car parking in front of their building. Similarly, one of the four principal aims for Dermatology Integrated Care in North Wales was to decentralise and to develop more community-based care close to patients' homes. Thus, all three services aimed to be higher in quality, lower in cost whilst also being more conveniently accessible.

How do these three examples of disruptive innovation in healthcare fare when looked at through the quality improvement lens of Don Berwick? All three models of care were clearly focused on being highly efficient; there's very little waste of any description here. All three models embraced the fundaments of patient flow through their services, with supply matching demand, and no bottle necks leading to delays; indeed, all three services are textbook examples of continuous flow. Two of the three services include teledermatology, whose principal benefit to a specialised clinical service is to reduce demand for clinic appointments; teledermatology patient referrals could be dealt with in high numbers efficiently and constructively, thereby freeing up clinical capacity for face-to-face services. All three models of care highlight numerical assessment of their service as surrogate markers for excellence. The three services succeed in matching capacity to demand, thereby avoiding the creation of waiting lists. The three services could only succeed if their value network was attuned and totally supportive to what they were trying to achieve. This requires a high degree of respect and trust between the commissioner of healthcare and the provider; by cooperating with each other, both managed to achieve what is important to themselves. Finally, Berwick urges us to never lose sight of the patient as the central figure; all three of these services place the patient in the middle, and are focused on providing excellent care which is convenient to access.

* * *

FEMALE, TWENTY-FIVE, SCALY RED RASH ON FACE

Ffion is twenty-five and has had a rash on the face for six weeks. It started under her nose, and then spread down the right upper lip onto the right cheek. It is bright red and scaly. The GP requests a routine appointment. Prior to Dermatology Integrated Care this would have involved a wait of over twelve months. Even now, a routine appointment takes twelve weeks. However, the referral letter includes photos, which allow me to assess the severity and to consider the diagnosis. Ffion needs to be seen without delay; I upgrade the referral to 'urgent'. The following week Ffion attends my evening clinic at Ysbyty Gwynedd. She tells me that she helps out on her boyfriend's farm in her spare time. It is apparent to me that Ffion has picked up an animal fungus from the cattle, so called 'ringworm', and now needs a potent anti-fungal tablet for treatment. Two months later, the rash has cleared, except for a slight pink shadow which is gradually fading.

CHAPTER 30

THE *BJD*

2013-2019

It was June 2013 and I was standing in for the editor at the *British Journal of Dermatology (BJD)* editorial board meeting. To chair such a meeting at a major international dermatology scientific research conference in Edinburgh, the biggest dermatology science conference in the world, held once every two years in rotation between Japan, Europe and the USA, presented the perfect opportunity to solicit opinions. I was editor-elect, and was keen to better understand how the *BJD* was regarded by the elite dermatology leaders and researchers; all were passionate about the science of skin disease. In the company of twenty professors from the UK and overseas, I was apprehensive, but expectant.

'Let's not waste time. What's wrong with the *BJD*, and how does Alex set about sorting it out?'

It was a useful intervention from a colleague designed to provoke a level of debate that, until now, had been missing from the meeting. He lit the blue touch paper and sat back to enjoy the fireworks, a vigorous exchange of thoughts and ideas about the place of the journal in academic publishing for dermatology. The *BJD* had a strong tradition of publishing scientific papers; however, in the discussions which ensued, the journal took a bit of a beating. The board members lost their inhibitions and began trying to outdo each other with their candour and insights. The accepted opinion amongst the group was that the *British Journal of Dermatology* was only third or fourth choice for their top dermatology science papers. We all knew it, yet it was still surprising to hear the truth.

As the meeting now began drawing to a conclusion, I was aware that not everyone had spoken. A soft voice filled a pause; it was a thoughtful and highly regarded clinical academic from Scotland.

'What is the point of the *BJD*? I am not clear what it is trying to do.'

•　•　•

Here was my cue. I decided to conduct an informal survey. I asked my colleagues in Newport how many of them read the *BJD* each month. To my amazement, not a single one of my six colleagues read it, despite receiving the journal each month. They were high calibre clinicians, some with national profiles for their expertise. If they didn't read the *BJD*, then who did? This was all the confirmation I needed that the journal had lost its way, appealing neither to the science professors at the top of the dermatology academic tree (except as a safe home for their lesser research outputs), nor to jobbing clinical dermatologists delivering high quality dermatology care to our local population. I too was left wondering: what was the point of the *BJD*?

In the following days, I studied the performance data for the journal over the previous ten years. Most of the performance indicators were fluctuating around a mean, which confirmed that the journal was not progressing, and had not done so for many years. Worldwide institutional subscriptions for the journal were static; the profitability of the journal was static; online downloads of individual articles were increasing, but not as fast as for competitor journals. Importantly, the performance indicator used to assess academic journals was the impact factor (a number generated each year as the number of times articles from the journal are cited by authors in a two-year window, divided by the number of published original articles in the same journal for the same two-year period), which was static; it had fluctuated up and down over the previous ten years, but had failed to make a sustained improvement. Unfortunately, many of the *BJD* rival journals had raised their game and improved their impact factors, leaving the *BJD* languishing in seventh place in the world rankings for dermatology journals. It was clear that a fundamental rethink was needed to underpin strategic change. Furthermore, if my time as editor was to be a success, the journal needed to again become essential reading for clinical dermatologists and a first-choice journal for submission of top dermatology scientific research.

I knew that the politics of change for the *British Journal of Dermatology* might be tricky, as the British Association of Dermatologists (BAD) was the owner of the journal, and was responsible for all the main decisions. Blaming the BAD for the journal's recent lacklustre performance was not an option; I needed to bring the BAD president and officers with me on a journey of change and renewal. This was particularly delicate as the president was himself a recent past editor of the journal. The journal's editorial board at that time was distant and remote from the power behind the *BJD*. By good fortune, the academic vice-president of the BAD, Professor Irene Leigh, was a senior and successful academic leader in British dermatology (she had been the president and lead organiser of the big scientific conference in Edinburgh a few months earlier). I shared my concerns about the journal with Irene and was encouraged to work on a strategy. Irene was well connected with academic dermatologists around the globe, and helped me to draft the strategy and recruit some fresh blood to the *BJD* editorial team. We were seeking younger rising stars, who would feel energised and committed to the journal as we sought to relaunch. I already had experience of writing five-year strategies and using them to deliver significant change, having done this twice before as director of R&D for Aneurin Bevan University Health Board, my NHS employer. I worked on early strategy drafts with Irene, and then shared my plans with other dermatology academics including Professor Nick Reynolds (Newcastle), Professor Chris Griffiths (Manchester), Professor Rod Hay (London) and Professor John McGrath (London). By the time I presented the strategy to the president and officers of the BAD, I had a carefully crafted document with a five-year programme of change. The ambition? To reposition the *BJD* and to re-establish the journal's identity. The aim was to make the journal relevant again to clinical dermatologists and academics around the globe. Success would be judged by the *BJD* becoming re-established as a top three dermatology journal, one of the elite.

It was Professor Nick Reynolds's idea to publish a position statement to be clear about the purpose of the journal. Nick joined me as co-author on the editorial published in June 2014, announcing the new *BJD*; henceforth, things would be different. I had known Nick since we were teenagers at medical school; he wasn't afraid to speak to me in forthright, uncompromising terms. He made it clear that we needed to recruit some high calibre researchers and statistics experts to the *BJD* editorial team.

'Like who?' I asked, when we were chatting at a big European dermatology conference in Amsterdam.

By chance, a passing guy in jeans, trainers, and a short stubble beard waved at Nick.

'Someone like him,' Nick said.

'Do you know him?' I was curious.

'Yes. He's Tamar Nijsten, from Rotterdam'

Professor Tamar Nijsten was head of dermatology at the Erasmus University Medical Center in Rotterdam. He was an epidemiologist (epidemiology is the study and analysis of the distribution, patterns and determinants of health and disease conditions in defined populations, the same speciality as Archie Cochrane), but had broad interests across the whole of dermatology. The new *BJD* strategy involved focusing on five areas of dermatology, by creating an editorial team which reflected this. Epidemiology was one of our chosen five priority areas. Although the *BJD* regularly published high quality epidemiology papers, the editorial team did not include any epidemiologists; the journal failed to project expertise in this important field.

A few days later, Nick and I spoke to Tamar by conference

call. We explained the new *BJD* strategy, and emphasised that epidemiology was one of five new areas of expertise we wanted to create for the journal. Would Tamar agree to join the journal as the Epidemiology section editor and help to recruit the rest of the 'epi' team? His role would include creating a *BJD* voice for epidemiology through regular editorials, and to oversee the peer review of papers submitted on epidemiology. He sounded pleased to have been asked, and accepted the invitation, but on condition that we also appointed his lead statistician. A few days later, Tamar had accepted a formal invitation to join the *BJD* team, along with his lead statistician Loes Hollestein. Things were moving fast, and the five-year strategy was already bearing fruit.

Over the course of the next two years the *BJD* editorial team, most of whom were unpaid, grew from sixteen members to sixty-five. We started with the section editors, like Tamar, and used them to help identify and recruit teams to work in their sections. It was networking on a grand scale, and took place at breakneck speed. By the time rival journals realised what we were doing, the process was complete; we had snapped up many rising stars in dermatology. I was following a classic leadership technique by surrounding myself with the brightest and best. We were also careful to strive for gender equality within the team, and to have an international team, with representation from across the globe (within the limitations of the global dermatology research community, which was certainly not globally representative).

Dr Fiona Godlee, editor of the *British Medical Journal (BMJ)*, had been a guest speaker for our annual editorial team meeting in London. The *BMJ* had steadily improved its impact factor by focusing on publishing fewer and better papers and adding more editorial and journalistic content to the journal. These principles were logical and easy to understand, but harder to emulate. We started with editorials. Few dermatology journals published regular editorials. After all, they are more work for the editor, and most editors are overworked and have tight deadlines. The last thing they needed were more tasks. I had to lead from the front, writing a monthly editorial myself for the first year, and then nurturing editorial writing within the new editorial team. Most of us had no experience in writing editorials, as they were not a prominent element of the *BJD* before this new era. We had to establish a house style, and develop a system for internal peer review, so that editorials were concise, thought-provoking, and well-crafted. Importantly, some of the editorials were linked to key papers in that particular issue, meaning we needed a fast and efficient process for generating editorials that would not delay the publication of these important papers. Prior to my term as editor, there might be three or four editorials each year in the twelve issues of the *BJD*. By the time I stepped down as editor six years later, we were publishing two or three editorials in every issue.

The steady and regular *BJD* editorials soon started to be noticed. They were drawing in the clinicians, and seemed to resonate with the readership. Some editorials concerned the journal, and what we were doing; others were linked to an important original article in the same issue; others concerned professional issues for clinical dermatologists; finally, some editorials concerned the ever-changing face of dermatology and dermatological clinical practice. In addition to appealing to the readership, these editorials not infrequently attracted citations. This came as no surprise, as they were often written by well-known, high-profile dermatologists. By giving the *BJD* a voice, it became something more than it had been; it now had a character and appealed to the readership at an emotional, and not just a scientific or clinical, level. It was now easier for our target audience to feel connected. The editorial team were passionate about what we were doing, which was clear from our editorials. It felt organic and alive, something we were all proud to be involved with. Importantly, the *BJD* was becoming a more effective instrument to improve patient care in dermatology across the globe.

One *BJD* editorial on the subject of surgical treatment of malignant melanoma drew an angry response from a group of senior UK plastic surgeons. They were incensed that it had been implied that plastic surgeons working in the private sector were sometimes doing a specialised test (called sentinel node biopsy) for personal financial gain. I discussed their letter with the editorial author, Dr Jane McGregor; we were not sure how best to respond. Should we publish their letter, which is what they wanted, but had the potential of pouring petrol on their flames of anger? Perhaps we should publish an apology? Or maybe we should offer to modify or remove the offending sentence with a post-publication correction? None of these options was enticing, and some carried the risk of capitulating to the moral outrage of these plastic surgeons. We took advice from a senior and experienced colleague who was expert in melanoma. We also took advice from Fiona Godlee, editor of the *BMJ*, who advised us to tough it out and not capitulate.

We decided to go with Fiona Godlee's advice. I made a special effort to engage with the plastic surgeons, speaking with the senior author on the phone, and ending on good terms. I knew he was ambitious; I made it clear that the *BJD* was keen to publish his work, and to include him as an editorial writer for the journal when the opportunity arose. I explained that controversy and debate were good for academia, so long as they were conducted in the right spirit with respect, moderation and scientific rigour. At the end of the call, he sounded placated. A few days later, they withdrew their letter. As Fiona had explained to Jane and me, they were bluffing, hoping their show of strength would make us blink; it didn't.

The five-year strategy I wrote with help from others was approved by the president and officers of the BAD. But there was a fundamental issue which had still to be resolved. The term of editor of the *BJD* was just three years; two years after gaining approval for my five-year strategy I would be stepping down as editor. I discussed this with Irene, the BAD academic vice-president; we agreed that part of the problem for the *BJD* was that editors were forced to demit just when they had learnt the job and were becoming effective. The term of editor needed to be increased; however, I could not push for this myself, as it would look like self-interest. I left it to Irene to deal with the politics. This was tricky, as some officers were opposed to extending my term of office as editor. In the end, it was fudged by changing the rules and allowing the editor to apply for a second three-year term, in open competition against all comers. I accepted this without comment; there was no other choice. I applied for the post, was interviewed, and then was appointed for a second three-year term.

By now the lack of governance was evident. Nothing was written down; it was all based on trust and precedents. In particular, it was hard to reconcile the academic ambitions of the journal with the power for decisions resting with the BAD president and officers, who tended to be clinicians, not top academics. The senior academics on the *BJD* editorial board, whose role was to guide the journal and help it succeed, had almost no input into these decisions. I discussed this with some of the editorial board members. Would they like to take responsibility for these major decisions, like choosing the next editor, or appointing the publisher, or helping to guide strategy? Yes, they would.

I started work on a governance document, defining the issues, and creating clarity regarding operational processes at the journal. I worked with the editorial board to make sure this document contained enough detail to avoid ambiguity, but was concise, clear and easy to understand. As with the five-year strategy, it was essential to have these senior members of the editorial board as co-authors. After multiple drafts, I was finally happy with the text of the governance document, and submitted it to the new president of the BAD. He was the ideal person to consider this governance document, being a clinical academic himself, but I was nervous about how it would be received; a significant shift in power was proposed, from the president and officers of the BAD, to the academics on the journal's editorial board.

It took nearly three months before they agreed to accept the governance document. One or two clauses were amended or removed before it was finally accepted and agreed upon. At last, we had standard operating procedures for the journal, where previously there were none. It was an impressive performance by the BAD, who relinquished most of their power and control over the journal in return for the expectation of a better performance. It was win-win-win, with the officers, the editor-in-chief and the editorial board all happy with the outcome.

As the end of my term as *BJD* editor approached, I reflected on my role. I'd always admired William Osler for his commitment to academic writing, and recall that he was the founding editor and figurehead for the *Quarterly Journal of Medicine*. The *QJM* is still a great journal 100 years later. What a privilege it was to follow so closely in Osler's footsteps.

* * *

The annual impact factors for the *BJD* were to be announced. Our publishers had calculated that the impact factor for the journal had leapt forward; we were awaiting official confirmation. I arrived at work and turned on my computer to find emails from across the world of dermatology congratulating me on the journal's success. The impact factor had been announced: 6.1, the highest in the journal's history. We were still ranked fourth, but snapping at the heels of our competitors. Twelve months later, the journal went one better; the impact factor rose to 6.7 and the journal was now ranked third. We had overtaken the previously pre-eminent dermatology science journal, which had for decades been the top dermatology journal.

I was delighted. Our strategy had worked; we had achieved what we had set out to do – the *BJD* had become relevant again to dermatologists throughout the world. By focusing on raising the quality of the papers that we accepted we had created something special that we were all proud of. Importantly, the original research that we were publishing was now cutting edge, making a difference to patient care for those with skin diseases. The *BJD* was back in the game.

●   ●   ●

TELEPHONE CONSULTATION
WITH ELDERLY FEMALE PATIENT

I conduct a telephone consultation during the COVID-19 crisis with an elderly female patient I do not know. We chat, and she warms to the interaction. We cover the medicine, and the call nears its conclusion. However, I feel I do not know her, particularly as the interaction is by telephone. I ask her who was with her in the lockdown.

'Just Duchess,' she replies. 'Duchess is my cat.'

'How lovely,' I reply, 'and what sort of cat is she?'

'She's a Persian crossed with a mixed breed, but could pass as a pedigree to the non-expert eye.'

'Duchess is much more affectionate since the death of my other cat.

'How sad to lose him,' I say. 'And what was he called?

'Marmaduke,' she replies. 'We already had a Duke, so the second cat had to be a Duchess.'

Of course.

CHAPTER 31

GETTING THE
WORD OUT

2019-2020

I was concerned that most dermatologists in Wales and in other parts of the UK were not aware of our new model of care, Dermatology Integrated Care. I discussed this with the team, including our managers. I suggested that we should consider entering the BMJ Dermatology Team of the Year, the same competition the Newport team I was part of had won in 2000. There would be multiple entries from across the UK and it seemed unlikely that our small, chronically under-resourced team would be shortlisted for this award when it was always won by high-performing dermatology units with lots of specialist services and superb facilities. But it was precisely the lack of resources and the tiny team which made our service change so compelling. If we could achieve outstanding performance with so little resource, then so could other units around the UK.

The entry form did not take long to complete.

Was the project innovative?

The World Health Organisation's definition of health innovation is to develop and deliver new or improved health policies, systems, products and technologies, and services and delivery methods that improve people's health. Importantly, health innovation adds value in the form of improved efficiency, effectiveness, quality, safety and/or affordability. Our project does this in relation to our local dermatology service. Although it is beyond the scope of this work to demonstrate that we have improved patients' health, we are confident that we have greatly improved our patients' access to healthcare.

Was the project original?

The unique and original element of this project was to bring the generalist and specialist teams together to function as one.

Did the intervention offer a new approach?

Confidence-building initiatives were required, including the Dermatology Integrated Care meetings in GP surgeries. These meetings last for two to three hours and involve members of the specialist team meeting with a group of GPs in their own surgeries. All GP surgeries in our area are visited once yearly for these meetings.

Our lead dermatologist had previously set up a patient advocacy group for dermatology in South Wales. This group, the Gwent Dermatology Patient Panel, were used to inform the new model of care in North Wales. Close attention was paid to how patients and local GPs reacted to the new service by focusing on their feedback and comments. Many patients said the single most important element of a specialist service was speed of access to that service.

Examples of two elements of the new service which have changed following patient and GP feedback:

1. The advice and guidance letters sent to patients are unique and are personalised. We considered standardised letters for particular conditions but opted to stick with personalised letters following positive patient feedback. Most patients say that a personalised letter from a consultant within two weeks is better than waiting for twelve months for a routine appointment.
2. Initially, advice and guidance letters were addressed to GPs only. It was then suggested they should be addressed to the patient, with the GP copied in. This simple change made a big difference to the acceptability and benefits of these letters, being better for both GPs and for patients.

A few weeks later, in February 2020, an email popped into my inbox from the *BMJ*. From a field of nearly twenty, we had been shortlisted to the final four. There was a delay of months due to COVID, then we were told to prepare a presentation – a ten-minute video about our service. There would also be a fifteen-minute online Q and A session with the *BMJ* judges. In November 2020, the big day came and our team performed well. Our weakness, I felt after the session, was the lack of patient involvement in setting up the new service. Nevertheless, I felt we were in with a chance.

Later that same day, the award ceremony took place online. We were doing an evening clinic in Llandudno General Hospital, so many of the team were together. The award was announced whilst I was seeing a patient. I worked out that the silence from the adjacent room suggested that we hadn't won. Still, we had made the cut and been included in very distinguished company. Well done to the winners (Dermatology at Chelsea and Westminster Hospital). They deserved their success.

* * *

MALE, FORTY-EIGHT, MULTIPLE SEBORRHOEIC KERATOSES

Danny is now a counsellor. He was a nurse, but gave it up as he found it too stressful. He set up as a masseur with essential oils, but realised that he enjoyed the chat more than the laying on of hands. Furthermore, the pay is better. Danny has a soft, gentle voice, and is naturally good at social interaction. He is single, now in his late forties, and still hopeful of finding a partner. He has lots of seborrhoeic keratoses: brown, scaly benign spots with a stuck-on appearance. Danny has hundreds of them. All over his back, thighs and tummy.

'They're hideous,' he tells me, 'but not nearly as bad as my mother's were. All I want is to see you privately, to treat them with cryotherapy every three or four months.'

I do about fifteen to twenty at a time. There is an endless supply. This treatment helps him to feel that 'I'm not turning into my mother.' He isn't ready to give up on his looks, especially as he is still dating.

CHAPTER 32

COVID

2020

Few can forget those strange days of early March 2020, when we prepared for the rise in COVID-19 cases and went into lockdown. For those first few days of the global pandemic, our immediate concern in dermatology was to gauge to what extent those patients taking immune-suppressing drugs to treat skin disease were now at risk. Luckily, the nine new clinical pathways we had introduced as part of Dermatology Integrated Care twelve months earlier had created a clinical system that was lean and efficient. As a consequence, our response to COVID-19 was rapid and easily coordinated. The whole clinical team participated; every patient was contacted by phone to discuss the issues. However, a persistent concern with all of these patients was uncertainty about how to convey the level of risk for each of these drugs. What exactly should we be saying?

At the same time, I received an email from the president of the British Association of Dermatologists, along with nine other UK dermatologists. Would I be willing to join a virtual national committee tasked with reaching a consensus about these dermatology immuno-suppressant drug issues in the context of the pandemic? We were informed that dermatologists from across the UK needed coherent and carefully considered recommendations concerning the immuno-suppressant drugs that we all prescribed. I was proud to have been chosen, immediately recognising the importance of this task; I readily accepted. I knew the nine other dermatologists well, through my previous role as editor of the *British Journal of Dermatology*.

Within two weeks we had created a grid to allow dermatologists to see at a glance the level of risk associated for each of the immuno-suppressant drugs: a high-risk group; intermediate risk; low risk. Once created, this grid was made available to all UK dermatologists. It was also included on the British Association of Dermatologists website, accessible across the globe. Importantly, it helped my team, and many other dermatology teams, to give informed and consistent advice to our patients who were receiving these drugs. Members of this committee were then asked if we would be willing to serve for the duration of the pandemic to reach consensus responses to ongoing drug-related issues. We all accepted this invitation, answering specific clinical questions arising from clinicians, for which there was no clear national guidance. This was important, linking immediately with frontline clinicians and patient care. It was interesting to see how this virtual committee resolved clinical issues relating to the immuno-suppressant drugs by rapid discussion and debate, sometimes by resorting to first principles. This was intuitive medicine at its best and exhilarating to be involved with.

Soon after lockdown had started, we discovered that Dermatology Integrated Care was ideally suited for the challenge of delivering high quality care to our patients with skin disease during a pandemic. Our waiting lists were already short and continued to fall. For our team, the transition to a new way of working was easy, as most of what was needed in terms of working differently had already happened.

By now members of neighbouring dermatology teams had discretely approached me for advice on how to change their services. They told me in confidence that their services were failing and that Dermatology Integrated Care was well suited to the new style of medicine in the COVID era. They knew that our waiting lists had continued to fall, whilst their services remained in crisis, with unacceptably long waiting lists, no plan and no strategy to take things forward. I felt guilty that our success had forced my colleagues to confront the shortcomings of their own clinical services. This was an unintended consequence of the innovation and service change taking place without their input or agreement within the same organisation.

Common sense prevailed, and within just a few months of the COVID-19 outbreak, there was general acceptance by the North Wales dermatologists that the core elements of Dermatology Integrated Care must be adopted if healthcare was to survive in the new world in which we found ourselves. The concept of trying to bridge the gap between the specialist and generalist teams was now accepted as essential, and tentative steps towards teledermatology were taking place across the whole health board. New ways of working and interacting with patients and GPs were being introduced, including web and telephone-based consultations.

●   ●   ●

AN OLD SOLDIER

He was in his late sixties but looked much older. I asked him what work he had done.

'I was in the army.'

'What regiment?'

'The Parachute Regiment.'

I knew their reputation. Like the SAS and the Marines they were an elite regiment, the cream of the British Army. I also knew about the stain on their reputation because of the civilian murders in Ballymurphy and Derry in August 1971.

'Were you in Northern Ireland?' I asked.

'Nine tours of duty,' he replied with pride.

'Anything else?' I asked.

'The Falkland Islands War.'

'How was that?'

'Fine, until we had to get off the QEII and face machine guns. Our commanding officer "H" was killed.'

'I hope you don't mind me asking?'

'Not at all,' he replied. 'Most people aren't interested. I like talking about it.'

'Tell me about your skin,' I asked.

It was a leg ulcer. He needed compression bandaging and regular dressing changes.

By coincidence, that evening on BBC news, it was reported that Boris Johnson had made an apology on behalf of the British Government for the nine civilian murders at Ballymurphy. It was done by phone, to a third party, not to the Ballymurphy families themselves. A bungled apology, according to the intended recipients. In fact, 'not an apology at all,' they said.

CHAPTER 33

A STRUGGLING NHS
2020-2021

According to the prime minister, 2020 was supposed to be a time of healing and coming together, an opportunity to move forward as a nation. New opportunities beckoned, we were told by the arch Brexiteers masquerading as the Conservative Party, for Global Britain. During the previous seventy-five years, we had become used to the United Kingdom being on top table: Stalin, Roosevelt and Churchill; a permanent seat on the United Nations Security Council; one of the first nations with a nuclear deterrent; a member of the world's leading economies; a top three economy in Europe; a key ally to the United States. We even did well in the Olympics, always near the top of the medal table. As a country, we were used to punching above our weight. The world took the UK seriously. When the US was challenged, it was usually the UK standing by her side. And the jewel in the crown for our national identity? It was, of course, the National Health Service, as celebrated at the 2012 London Olympics opening ceremony. Free at the point of delivery; paid for by taxation; the ultimate act of levelling up. Sure, it had become a bit tatty around the edges; there were just too many patients. But our heroic doctors and nurses were doing their best. It was worth waiting for world-class health care.

However, this national treasure was a Labour Party concept. The electorate knew it, and the Tories knew they knew it. As a result, at every subsequent election, the Conservatives had to be clear about where they stood on the NHS. Could they be trusted?

In the 2010 general election David Cameron, the Conservative Party leader, campaigned on the slogan 'The NHS is safe in our hands'. What followed was the longest period of under-funding for the NHS since its inception. The hospitals fell into disrepair, leaking roofs were patched up, not replaced, capital equipment was not replaced and updated, the infrastructure for healthcare failed to adapt to the changes in health care delivery, not enough staff were trained and appointed. Scandal after scandal occurred with elderly and vulnerable patients left to die from neglect, prompting two public enquiries.

Despite all of this, there continued to be an assumption within the UK that we still had a world-class health service. In fact, cynical and unscrupulous politicians soon realised that commitments to spending on the NHS was a sure-fire vote winner. The Leave campaign promised 350 million pounds per week for the NHS, turning the referendum on leaving Europe into a vote about investment into the NHS. In the 2019 general election, Boris Johnson's Conservatives promised to build forty new hospitals. More empty promises.

Never had the country been so polarised. Never had political discourse been so polarising. And what followed would hit the cash-strapped NHS harder than anything previously encountered in our country. Covid.

* * *

When the UK recorded one of the highest death rates associated with COVID-19 globally, perhaps most shocking of all was the news that the Conservative government had failed to heed the recommendations of the pandemic rehearsal enacted in 2016. This failure had consequences. It was intended to test our readiness for such a threat and to produce clear recommendations on what needed to be done. Other factors to explain the UK's higher than expected death rate suggested by Richard Horton, editor of the *Lancet*, included a political class distracted by Brexit that had failed to put well-being and equity at the heart of its policies; deepening socioeconomic inequalities had made certain groups especially vulnerable to the infection; long-standing disinvestment in the public sector which had left the health and social care systems in particular jeopardy; generally poor population health which meant that many communities were poorly protected against this new and dangerous virus. These were, undoubtedly, four important reasons. Other factors included a general lack of pandemic preparedness; poor political leadership during the pandemic; long-term NHS staff shortages; delayed implementation of physical distancing measures; poor supplies of personal protective equipment; poor coordination with local authorities and public health teams; a dysfunctional track and trace system; absence of coordination between the devolved nations; and poor decisions around hospital discharge to care homes.

A number of positives did emerge from the NHS response to COVID-19. There was the impressive planning and capacity-building for intensive care, our 'Don Berwick moment', with a sharp focus on understanding and managing patient flow through the system. Although the system creaked, and came close to grid-lock, that nightmare scenario never happened. Secondly, there was the superb and unflinching care delivered by NHS doctors, nurses and ancillary staff, invoking the very best of our greatest role models from history, William Osler, Betsi Cadwaladr and Florence Nightingale. But although all of us working in health and social care knew that the NHS had been underfunded for years, it still came as a shock to discover that the UK death rate from COVID-19 was so much higher than for most other countries.

Something unconscionable then spang to mind: perhaps the NHS was no longer world class?

In May 2021, the *Lancet* published a paper on the future of the NHS. A commission had been convened three years earlier in collaboration with the London School of Economics and Political Science (LSE). Their report had been delayed and modified due to the pandemic. In order to understand the full picture, the authors had painstakingly collected data on health and health-care from other developed countries with similar health systems: fifteen European countries and the non-European members of G7. This created a ranking from best to worst for the eighteen countries included. So, how did the UK do?

Here are the UK results, out of eighteen:

- Life expectancy of the total population at birth: 15th
- Infant mortality per 1,000 live births: 15th
- Five-year cancer survival, standardised by age:
  - » Colon cancer: 16th
  - » Breast cancer: 13th
  - » Lung cancer: 15th
  - » Prostate cancer: 14th
- Thirty-day mortality rate for acute myocardial infarction: 9th
- Thirty-day mortality rate for ischaemic stroke: 10th
- Proportion of GDP spent on healthcare: 9th
- Health expenditure per capita: 13th
- Proportion of GDP spent on welfare: 14th
- Practicing nurses per 1,000 people: 10th
- Practicing doctors per 1,000 people: 13th
- Hospital beds per 1,000 people: 17th
- MRI scanners per million population: 17th
- CT scanners per million population: 17th
- Income inequality with comparator countries: 17th
- Top three performances: None

This data represents the moment when the UK must face up to the fact that competitor countries have left us behind. We are no longer one of the best for healthcare. Indeed, for many of these indices, we are among the worst. There will be no quick fixes. A period of reflection and debate is now needed. The *Lancet* Commission on the Future of the NHS believes that this grim position can be turned around, and our health service can be great again; they explicitly map out what needs to be done to achieve this. Our political leaders must now be strategic, and have a long-term plan. If success as a nation in health and healthcare is important, we must now invest in people, systems and facilities. It will not be cheap, but it will create a fairer and healthier society.

*   *   *

On 28 February 2020 Martin Landray, an Oxford University professor, sent an email to the director of the Wellcome Trust, a medical research charity, asking the question: was anyone thinking about randomised trials for COVID-19 treatment?

Because if we don't, then lots of drugs will get thrown at lots of patients, and we will be none the wiser about whether any of them work or don't, or are even causing harm.

There it was; the Archie Cochrane moment, right at the onset of the global pandemic, where it needed to be. Two weeks later, a study protocol was ready. In contrast to the UK government, the UK's life sciences responded well to the global pandemic. In less than four months the RECOVERY trial had identified a cheap and effective COVID-19 treatment, saving millions of lives worldwide. In less than twelve months, it had found another, tocilizumab, and ruled out four more, including hydroxychloroquine, a drug promoted by Donald Trump. This study applied the methods extolled by Archie Cochrane to answer critical questions relating to COVID-19 patient care, within short time periods. Some 185 hospital sites were enrolled, an extraordinary achievement in the face of the day-to-day pressures of patient care during the pandemic. The RECOVERY trial was huge, and was set up and ready to go as the first wave hit. Britain's chief medical officers had already written to every UK hospital urging them to take part, which they did. The irony is that the circumstances that led to the UK suffering so many cases of COVID-19 also created the opportunity for vast clinical trials. What clinical trials need are patients; unfortunately, the NHS had plenty.

The Osier moment also came at the start of the pandemic. The COVID-19 Genomics UK Consortium was set up in April 2020; it identified well over 1,000 different importation events with infected people arriving in the UK from China, Spain, France and Italy. UK research laboratories soon became home to the majority of the world's genetic sequencing of COVID-19. This unprecedented sequencing effort allowed mutations to be identified and tracked, as researchers sought to understand how such changes affected transmission of the virus and response to vaccination. Most of this sequencing was done at the Wellcome Sanger Institute in Cambridge, a not-for-profit British research institute primarily funded by the Wellcome Trust. Like Dr Faith Osier had personally done when mapping antigens on the malaria organism, this enormous genetic sequencing initiative was aiming to fully understand the biology of COVID-19: 'If you know the enemy and know yourself, you need not fear the result of a hundred battles.'

The COVID-19 AstraZeneca vaccine was created at Oxford University's Jenner Institute by a team of scientists led by Professor Sarah Gilbert. This was the UK's 'Jenner moment' during the pandemic, rapidly applying the very best scientific minds to vaccine development, within a research institute that had been created exactly for this task. In less than twelve months the vaccine had been developed, trialled, manufactured and approved for clinical use. The vaccine is now being manufactured at twenty-five different sites, in fifteen countries. It was a remarkable achievement, and ensured that Jenner's name resonated worldwide, a fitting tribute to this inspirational historical figure.

Finally, the UK's rapid purchasing of vaccines and implementation of a national vaccination programme was nimble and effective when compared with the slow and heavy-footed earlier responses by UK government. The venture capitalist Kate Bingham lead the COVID-19 vaccine procurement process; her committee agreed deals for 340 million doses of vaccine from six different companies. Furthermore, the UK regulatory framework was streamlined to allow much speedier approval for these vaccines once they became available. The UK was the world's first country to embark upon a mass immunisation programme in December 2020, almost exactly twelve months after the first cases of COVID-19 were diagnosed and reported from China. The coordination of mass vaccination has been complex, and not without problems; despite this, the UK has led the way in terms of speed of uptake of vaccination by the population. The NHS and a network of volunteers have been credited with this success.

* * *

The Grange University Hospital in Cwmbran, South Wales was the first brand new hospital to open in the UK following the onset of the pandemic; this was April 2020. I had been associate medical director at this health board for thirteen years. Along with many others, I was heavily involved in the planning and patient flow discussions for this new hospital; I knew all about the costs. The whole process had taken just under twenty years to complete, from first discussions to first patients over the threshold. But this hospital was different; it was a specialist and critical care centre, with no open wards, just rooms with single beds, and no outpatient facilities. As a result, the cost of this hospital, at 350 million pounds, was lower than the 500 million usually required to build a conventional new hospital with outpatient facilities.

Forty new hospitals in England was a large commitment for the Conservative Party to make during the 2019 general election. Of course, forty new hospitals is headline-grabbing, a sound bite which is easy to remember and to repeat. When the funding for these forty new hospitals was finally announced by the prime minister in October 2020, it was just 3.7 billion pounds. A simple calculation, based on the cost of the brand-new Grange University Hospital, reveals this figure would only buy ten of these new stripped-down and outpatient-free hospitals, not forty. For a new 500-million-pound hospital with outpatient facilities, 3.7 billion would buy just seven, not forty.

One of the forty hospitals on the list was Charing Cross Hospital, my old medical school. It was to be refurbished floor by floor; clearly not a new hospital at all. Another on the list was the new cancer centre at the Royal United Hospital in Bath, where I had just accepted a new job (I moved to Bath in May 2021). On my way to and from work each day, I studied the posters on the white temporary hoarding erected around this building site to see what it said: 'Dyson Cancer Centre' was writ large; nowhere did it say 'New Hospital'. The political rhetoric did not match the bricks and mortar reality. This was a con, with the voting public and NHS workers being treated as mugs.

* * *

The COVID-19 pandemic has revealed some wonderful positives about UK life sciences, and the excellence of NHS staff. However, it has also highlighted that the NHS has been diminished under recent successive governments, and is no longer world-class. There was no 'Julian Tudor Hart moment' to celebrate in the pandemic because social justice and inequality are not at the core of the NHS; in fact, it was exactly the opposite. Julian Tudor Hart wrote the inverse care law based on his analysis of the UK National Health Service fifty years ago. The relevance of his observation remains as important today as it was in 1970. I have experienced this first hand in my recent move from a job in Bangor, where we had very little, to Bath, where we have a lot. There remains an imperative for the systems within the National Health Service to counter such inequality and lack of fairness.

The NHS has become tired and in places threadbare. Our innovation in North Wales was a case in point, best summarised as doing more with not enough. Although patient access to our service was transformed, our facilities were basic, well below the norm. Our strategy was to create new day-treatment hubs within the communities we served, providing first-class facilities that were closer to our patients. These day-treatment centres would be run by our nurses, and would offer state-of-the-art facilities for skin cancer surgery, allergy testing, wound care, teaching patients about topical treatments, and ultraviolet light therapies. We even created a home phototherapy service, offering ultraviolet light therapies for patients in their own homes, for those who lived remotely to our community treatment hubs, or who were unable to attend. Additionally, we planned to join forces with plastic surgery and maxillofacial surgery to create a new shared surgical facility at our main hospital for the treatment of skin cancer. These plans were not over-ambitious, but they would require investment if we were to create first-class facilities. There was no sign of the necessary funds or even recognition of the need for this modest investment by the end of 2021. Ultimately, doing more with not enough is an empty philosophy which short-changes healthcare.

The NHS now needs strategic leadership and investment as well as innovation. Most importantly, it needs to reconnect to the values articulated by Nye Bevan that made it such a great and unifying concept. Sadly, the essence of Bevan's NHS has been gradually lost by creeping privatisation. Perhaps the most important element of the COVID-19 pandemic was to hold a mirror up to the NHS; what was reflected back was hardly a surprise, but was still a shock to us all.

So what must the NHS now do to survive? In short, it should heed the seven following recommendations of the independent and non-politically aligned LSE–*Lancet* Commission on the future of the NHS:

Recommendation 1: increase investment in the NHS, social care, and public health. They recommend that NHS funding increase by a minimum of 4 per cent a year in real terms over at least the next ten years.

Recommendation 2: improve resource management across health and care at national, local and treatment levels. The LSE–*Lancet* Commission recommend that decisions on resource allocation should be underpinned by sound principles and robust methods and that a strategic view is taken of the long term. This should address healthcare inequality, and the need to address the inverse care law.

Recommendation 3: develop a sustainable, skilled, and inclusive health and care workforce to meet challenging health and care needs. Strategic implementation will require money and changes in emphasis on the health, morale, and well-being of the health and care workforce.

Recommendation 4: strengthen prevention of disease and disability and preparedness to protect against threats to health.

Recommendation 5: improve diagnosis in circumstances where evidence exists to support early diagnosis, for improved outcomes and reduced inequalities.

Recommendation 6: develop the culture, capacity, and capabilities of the NHS and social care to become a national learning health and care system.

Recommendation 7: improve integration between health, social care, and public health and across different providers, including the third sector.

Healthcare must now move to the top of the political agenda if things are to change. Only the public can decide which political party should take on such an important responsibility, but past performance offers an important clue about who to trust with this task.

If the LSE–*Lancet* Commission recommendations are heeded, I can imagine in future years the creation of a more efficient and collaborative NHS service, as extolled by Berwick; an NHS as imagined by Lloyd George and as created by Bevan, where high quality healthcare is a fundamental right, an expectation, not a luxury; an NHS that is prepared and ready for the next pandemic, true to the spirit of Jenner and the pioneering work of Osier, not cringing in their shadows; an NHS which values care and respect for all patients and NHS staff, as exemplified by Osler; an NHS which encourages and nurtures innovation as described and exemplified by Christensen and Berwick; an NHS guided by the evidence for what really works in healthcare, as advocated by Cochrane. An NHS that works for all of us, consigning Tudor Hart's inverse care law to a footnote in history, never again to be a *Lancet* front-page headline.

And Betsi?

Where does Betsi fit into this vision of the future NHS?

I decided to pay her a visit to find out.

•   •   •

AN ELDERLY EX-CIVILIAN PILOT

He is badly sun-damaged, and a regular in our department. Now seventy-nine, he had been a civilian airline pilot. Even at this age, he is slim and moved lightly on his feet. Still suave, he dresses with style. He looks the part.

'How did you get such badly sun-damaged skin?' I asked him when we first met.

'Years working in the tropics with BEA, BOAC and then BA.'

He had been based in the tropics, flying to Africa, the Far East and Australia. 'In those days, we used to lie in the sun for hours as we relaxed together between flights. We all did it.'

He tells me about the BOAC pilot reunions. 'It's just a load of old guys talking about the past. We've all got sun damage. We even compare notes about treatments we have received and tell each other the latest from our dermatologists.'

CHAPTER 34

HOPE FOR
THE FUTURE

2021

A bney Park cemetery in Stoke Newington is one of seven
London cemeteries established in the nineteenth century
to relieve overcrowding in local parish burial grounds. Before
it became a cemetery it had been laid out as an arboretum
and park, still evident by its sweeping paths and mature trees.
I had a map with directions from the cemeteries department
of Hackney Borough Council. This graveyard was now a local
nature reserve; Moli and I were enjoying the wildlife. Moli was
particularly interested in the grey squirrels on the ground under
the oaks and beech trees.

Eventually, we found the gravestone. Betsi had been buried
in the paupers' section of the cemetery in 1860, ignominious
for someone so important. There are no records to say who had
been present at her burial. I felt sure that Betsi's sister Bridget
would have been there. Surely a London-based Welsh Methodist
or Baptist minister would have presided over the internment?

Betsi and Bridget were daughters of a well-known North Wales preacher; their childhood had been spent in a Christian household, the Welsh bible ever present as a source of example, inspiration and wonder. It was probably those bible stories describing events overseas which had inspired awe in Betsi as a child, making her subsequent life of adventure more likely.

Betsi had ended up in a pauper's grave far from her beloved Wales. To take her body back to Bala would have been expensive, and was probably beyond Bridget's means. Betsi was never good with money, and had made no provision for funeral arrangements. Her principal lifetime earnings, accumulated from years of service in support of an ocean-crossing sea captain, were swindled from her in a London property deal soon after Betsi renounced life on the seas. A few years later she was bequeathed a substantial sum by a gentleman whom she had care for, only to be denied by his family who contested the will. She was also paid at a very low rate by Florence Nightingale, despite outstanding service and personal sacrifice in the Crimean War.

The gravestone was simple and fairly new, having been replaced in 2012. A light grey stone shield shape, tapering to a point at the top.

BETSI

CADWALADR

1789–1860

'Y ffyddlonaf o Nyrsys Ei Mawrhydi'

'The Faithfulest of Her Majesty's Nurses'

I listened to the birdsong and contemplated Betsi's life and what it had meant to me. I laid two leeks on the grave, my small tribute to Betsi (daffodils were out of season). Moli and I then retraced our steps, leaving me feeling oddly optimistic and hopeful for the challenges ahead.

As we headed home, I reflected on how Godfrey Morgan's experiences of visiting his wounded men in the hospital at Balaclava had made him aware of the importance of good quality healthcare. Forty-one thousand British combatants: 2,755 killed in action; 1,847 died of wounds; 17,580 died of disease. Disease was the killer, not shrapnel. We all know that now. Seeing this for himself must surely have had a profound effect on the young Godfrey, just four years out of Eton. Understanding this makes it easier to explain Godfrey's extraordinary role in helping to create a network of hospitals for the population of South East Wales. Furthermore, it was his own involvement with these very hospitals which was to inspire the young Nye Bevan to dream about a national health service. Once established, this NHS would then inspire Archie Cochrane and Julian Tudor Hart to create their own visions of how healthcare in the UK must be developed for the common good. It would also allow Faith Osier to complete her training as a paediatrician in Liverpool before becoming a researcher at one of the UK's top research institutes. A series of amazing contributions, each one leading to the next, up to the present day; all starting with Betsi Cadwaladr at Balaclava.

Thank you, Betsi.

BETSI
CADWALADR

1789-1860

FURTHER READING

Richard Barker. *2030 – The Future of Medicine: Avoiding a Medical Meltdown.* Oxford University Press (2011).

Derrick Baxby. *Jenner's Smallpox Vaccine: The Riddle of Vaccinia Virus and its Origins.* Heinemann Educational Books (1981).

R. Meredith Belbin. *Management Teams: Why they Succeed or Fail.* Routledge, Taylor Francis Group (2010).

John Berger. *A Fortunate Man: The Story of a Country Doctor.* Vintage Books (1997).

Donald M. Berwick. *Escape Fire: Designs for the Future of Health Care.* Jossey-Bass (2004).

Michael Bliss. *William Osler: A Life in Medicine.* Oxford University Press (1999).

Tim Brown. *Change by Design: How Design Thinking Transforms Organizations and Inspires Innovation.* Harper Business (2009).

Julia Cartwright and Sally Crowe. *Patient and Public Involvement Toolkit.* Wiley-Blackwell (2011).

Rita Charon. *Narrative Medicine: Honoring the Stories of Illness.* Oxford University Press (2006).

Clayton M. Christensen. *The Innovator's Dilemma: When New Technologies Cause Great Firms to Fail.* Harvard Business Review Press (1997).

Clayton M. Christensen, with Jerome Grossman and Jason Hwang. *The Innovator's Prescription: A Disruptive Solution for Healthcare.* McGraw Hill (2009).

Archie Cochrane. *Effectiveness and Efficiency: Random Reflections on Health Services.* The Royal Society of Medicine Press (1972).

—. *One Man's Medicine: An Autobiography of Professor Archie Cochrane.* The University Press, Cambridge (1989).

Complex Systems Modelling Group. *Modelling in Healthcare.* American Mathematical Society (2010).

Jim Collins. *Good to Great: Why Some Companies Make the Leap... and Others Don't.* Random House Business Books (2001).

A. J. Cronin. *The Citadel.* Vista (1937).

Nigel Crisp. *Turning the World Upside Down: The Search for Global Health in the 21st Century.* Royal Society of Medicine Press (2010).

F. Dawtry Drewitt. *The Life of Edward Jenner: Naturalist, and Discoverer of Vaccination.* Cambridge University Press (First published 1933. This compilation 2013).

Nicholas Dunkas (transl). *The Works of Hippocrates.* Diachronic Publications (1998).

Irmengarde Eberle and Henry S. Gillette. *Edward Jenner and Smallpox Vaccination.* Franklin Watts (1962).

Ben Goldacre. *Bad Science.* Fourth Estate (2008).

Jeff Dyer, Hal Gregersen, Clayton Christensen. *The Innovator's*

DNA; Mastering the Five Skills of Disruptive Innovators. Harvard Business Review Press (2011).

Roger Fisher, William Ury, Bruce Patton. *Getting to Yes: Negotiating Agreement Without Giving In.* Penguin Books (1981).

Arthur W. Frank. *The Wounded Storyteller: Body, Illness, and Ethics.* University of Chicago Press (1997).

David Gilbert. *The Patient Revolution: How We Can Heal the Healthcare System.* Jessica Kingsley Publishers (2020).

Trisha Greenhalgh. *How to Read a Paper: The Basics of Evidence-Based Medicine and Healthcare.* Wiley Blackwell (2019).

Fred J. Harries. *Viscount Tredegar.* (1908)

Roy Hattersley. *David Lloyd George: The Great Outsider.* Little, Brown (2010).

Adam Kay (ed.). *Dear NHS: 100 Stories to Say Thank You.* Trapeze (2020).

Gwyneth Lewis. *A Hospital Odyssey.* Bloodaxe Books (2010).

Peter Littlejohns and Michael Rawlings. *Patients, the Public and Priorities in Healthcare.* Radcliffe Publishing (2009).

Henry Marsh. *Do No Harm: Stories of Life, Death and Brain Surgery.* Phoenix (2014).

Michael Marmot. *The Health Gap: The Challenge of an Unequal World.* Bloomsbury (2015).

Annie McKee, Richard Boyatzis, Frances Johnston. *Becoming a Resonant Leader.* Harvard Business Press (2008).

Max Pemberton. *Trust Me: I'm a (Junior) Doctor.* Hodder (2008).

Roy Porter. *Blood and Guts: A Short History of Medicine.* Allen Lane, an imprint of Penguin Books (2002).

Steve Radcliffe. *How to make a bigger difference by leading at work and at home.* Pearson Books (2010).

Philip Rhys Evans. *A Country Doctor's Commonplace Book: Wonders and Absurdities.* Slightly Foxed Ltd. (2018).

Boaz Ronen and Joseph Pliskin. *Focused Operations Management for Health Services Organisations.* Jossey-Bass (2006).

Mark E. Silverman, T. Jock Murray, Charles S. Bryan (eds). *The Quotable Osler.* American College of Physicians (2003).

Nicklaus Thomas-Symonds. *Nye: The Political Life of Aneurin Bevan.* I. B. Tauris (2015).

Eric Topol. *Deep Medicine: How Artificial Intelligence Can Make Healthcare Human Again.* Basic Books (2019).

Julian Tudor Hart. *A New Kind of Doctor: The General Practitioner's Part in the Health of the Community.* Merlin Press (1988).

—. *The Political Economy of Health Care: A Clinical Perspective.* The Policy Press (2006).

Abraham Verghese. *Cutting for Stone.* Vintage Books (2010).

Graham Watt. *The Exceptional Potential of General Practice: Making a Difference in Primary Care.* CRC Press (2019).

David Widgery. *Some lives! A GP's East End.* Sinclair-Stevenson (1991).

Jane Williams (ed). *Betsy Cadwaladyr: A Balaclava Nurse. An Autobiography of Elizabeth Davis.* 1857. Honno (2015).

ACKNOWLEDGEMENTS

There are many people to thank and acknowledge in the creation of this book, including the following:

Chris Anstey, Andrew Jarvis, Jemima Hunt.

The dermatology team Betsi Cadwaladr University Health Board (West), probably the largest integrated dermatology team in the UK, especially: Andy Macfarlane, who led the charge with his pioneering attempts at working as a single-handed consultant in Bangor, Otilia Azamfirei, Habibah Ayab, Shahnawaz Khalil, Sian Morgan, Jonathan Bertalot, Jane Smith, Allison Browne, Miriam Williams, Rhian Ellis, Jane Jones, Gail Harris, Sarah Fostersmith. Tish Williamson. Alaw Jones, Bethan Jones, Eleri Roberts, Maria Roberts, Alison Kemp, Chris Subbe, the dermatology outpatient clinic nurses (especially Mrs Hughes, who never told me her first name), the physios who ran photo-therapy in Bangor, Holyhead, Ysbyty Alltwen and Llandudno, and the 350 GPs, salaried GPs, practice nurses, advanced nurse practitioners, specialist nurses, locum GPs, physician associates, and GP registrars on Anglesey, Gwynedd and Conwy who joined us in that unifying concept of Dermatology Integrated Care. The outpatient nurses at Ysbyty Gwynedd (especially Mrs

Hughes), Llandudno General Hospital, Ysbyty Alltwen, Ysbyty Bryn Beryl, and Ysbyty Penros Stanley.

The 'higher-ups', including Jo Whitehead, Andrew Goodall, Arpan Guha and Chris Stockton.

Those who have taught me, and who continue to teach me.

Those I have worked with in the multiple jobs described in this book.

My new consultant colleagues in Bath, Inma Mauri-Sole, Sarah Woodrow, Caoimhe Fahy, Naila Dinani and Sarah Rasool.

Students I have taught throughout my career.

Dermatologists in North Wales, even those who hated my ideas.

Former colleagues in South Wales, in particular Mabs Chowdhury, Richard Motley, Richard Goodwin, Natalie Stone, Tracy Bale, Chris Edwards, Jane Jones, Margaret Smith, Vivienne Watson, Joy Hayes, Helen Edwards, Bev Gambles, Nic Tarran, Colin Long, Ann Davies, Andrew Finlay, Maureen Chawla, Caroline Mills, Dafydd Roberts, Richard Logan, Sean Lanigan, Sharon Blackford, Ronnie Marks, Cilla Greedy and Barry Statham.

Colleagues at Cardiff University especially James Birchall, Julie Brown, John Bligh, Kamila Hawthorne, Steve Riley, Paul Harper, Vincent Knight, Janet Williams, Julie Vile, Penny Holborn, Izabela Spernaes (née Komeda), Kayne Putnam and Harriet Jones.

My old colleagues at Aneurin Bevan University Health Board, including all involved with dermatology: Stephen Hunter, Sue Bale, Rosz Howell, Grant Robinson, Paul Buss, Howell Jones, Gerald Anderson, Howell Lloyd, Owain Gibby, John Mason,

Tracy Bale, Liz Freeman, Kim Wynes, Jen Patterson, Jenny Isaac, Linda Collins, Linda Atwell.

Those who helped with patient advocacy, including all of the patients who became involved, especially Pam Fudge, Mayda and Paul Thomas and Peter Lapsley.

Those who helped me with the *BJD*, especially Irene Leigh, Tanya Bleiker, David Eedy, Nick Lavelle, Hywel Williams, David de Berker, Nick Reynolds, John McGrath, Chris Griffiths, Zheng Jie, Rod Hay, Sam Davies, Maria Khan, Rupert Cousins, Shenaz Ahmed, John Ingram, Jide Ibitoye, John Caulfield, Catherine Smith, the whole *BJD* editorial team.

Terrence Ryan, Gerry Jackson, Caroline Fertleman, Julian Godlee, Fiona Godlee and Jane MacGregor.

Russel Emmerson and Tom Millard.

The patients our team cared for in North Wales, who responded so positively when the system was changed. Your gratitude was reward enough for our endeavours.

Professor Andrew Finlay (again) and Dr Julia Scofield for your feedback and support as the book neared the finishing line, and for writing the foreword to the book. Your encouragement was essential in keeping me motivated to complete the task.

Dill Anstey, my sister, for inviting me each year to speak to sixth-formers at the Harris Academy in London about a career in medicine. This was what started me reflecting about my own career in medicine, and the people whom I revered. Dill also found critical readers from the ranks of prospective medical students at Harris Academy.

Paul Dawson, my brother-in-law, for helping to create the audio version of this book and my author's website.

My sister Charlotte and my sister-in-law Catherine, for supporting me emotionally at critical points on this creative journey.

My mother Denyse, who at the age of ninety-two is now completely blind. Denyse listened to the book as read to her by my brother Chris. Her body language during this reading conveyed her inner thoughts, as she tut-tutted the wicked Tories, nodded in agreement as the author offered solutions, and laughed in triumph as the waiting lists fell. She has promised to order lots of copies of my book to give to her many friends.

Paul Grant, from BBC Manchester, for your constructive feedback and comments.

John Gunson, my wife's cousin, a conscientious and constructive critical reader.

Our children Becca and Ben for listening to and supporting me whilst I was suffering from book-writing fever, that strange state of obsession and compulsion that engulfed me as I attempted to finish the task.

Sarah, my beloved wife. This book is about me, but by extension, it is about you too. The person I have become in thirty-three years of marriage has been shaped by our shared experiences as you have supported my career and created a loving and nurturing home within which our family could grow.

Moli the dog, who shared parts of this journey and barked at the delivery men bringing me more books.

Permissions for use of quotes: Cardiff University for quotes from One Man's Medicine by Archie Cochrane; Bristol University Press for quotes from The Political Economy of Healthcare by Julian Tudor Hart; Honno publishing for quotes from Betsy Cadwaladyr: A Balaclava Nurse; Harper Business, for quote from Change by Design by Tim Brown; Jossey-Bass for quotes from Escape Fire by Donald Berwick.

p.21 Crimean War: aerial view of the Castle Hospital, Balaclava. Lithograph after Lady Alicia Blackwood. Wellcome Collection. Public Domain Mark.

INDEX